# BOTANICAL SKIN CARE RECIPE BOOK, SECOND EDITION

**Published by Herbal Academy**
24 South Road, Bedford, MA 01731
Copyright © 2019 Herbal Academy

*theherbalacademy.com*

Marlene Adelmann, Founder of the Herbal Academy

Illustrators:
Amber Meyers
Emay Allmendinger

Editors:
Annie Hall
Dawn Costa, B.S., B.B.A
Jane Metzger, M.S.
Linden de Voil, RH(AHG)
Lisa Olson, RH(AHG)

Recipe Contributors:
Angela Justis
Ayo Ngozi Drayton, M.S.
Colleen Bingham Solis
Greta Kent-Stoll, AP(NAMA)
Heather Irvine
Jane Metzger, M.S.
Joseph Mulhollen, M.S.
Kelly Cable
Linden de Voil, RH(AHG)
Lisa Olson, RH(AHG)
Velda Thomas

International Standard Book Number
978-1-950671-02-1

# Botanical
# SKIN CARE
## Recipe Book

# ACKNOWLEDGMENTS

I cannot express enough thanks to my Herbal Academy team for their dedicated hard work, continued support, and encouragement: Ayo Ngozi Drayton, M.S., Colleen Bingham Solis, Greta Kent-Stoll, AP(NAMA), Heather Irvine, Jane Metzger, M.S., Joseph Mulhollen, M.S., Kelly Cable, Linden de Voil, RH(AHG), Lisa Olson, RH(AHG), Velda Thomas, my sincere thanks for everything that you contributed in making this project a reality.

Amber Meyers and Emay Allmendinger, your beautiful illustrations and tremendous dedication and hard work made this book come to life—my sincerest appreciation.

As always to my editors: Annie Hall, Dawn Costa, B.S., B.B.A, Jane Metzger, M.S., Linden de Voil, RH(AHG), Lisa Olson, RH(AHG)—thank you. To all my fellow herbalists over at Perch, we could not have offered these recipes without having tested them for accuracy, effectiveness, or lusciousness (someone had to do it, right?). Jane was our master recipe maker with help from many of our HA family including Emily Lacouture and Thavi Sivongxai from our Media Department and little hands Ava, Lila, Lyon, Rose, and Zak—there were many willing to lather up and dip into dreamy lotions and moisturizers, including myself!

To everyone who contributed to and worked behind the scenes of the Botanical Skin Care Course which inspired such a book, the completion of this project could not have been accomplished without your perseverance and support. Angela, Meagan, Michelle—you are a gift to the Herbal Academy and our students.

And finally, to our authors, for creating such wonderful and thoughtful recipes and making this project truly possible.

My heartfelt and most sincere thanks.

**MARLENE ADELMANN**
FOUNDER OF THE HERBAL ACADEMY

# TABLE OF CONTENTS

*Maintaining a daily skin care routine can also be a self-care practice of loving the skin you're in.*

BOTANICAL SKIN CARE COURSE

# INTRODUCTION

*Welcome to the Botanical Skin Care Recipe Book!*

At first glance, skin may seem like a minor player compared to critical internal organs like the heart, lungs, or brain; after all, the skin is such an everyday part of you, hanging out in plain view! But take just a moment to reflect on all the incredible things your skin is doing 24 hours a day.

For starters, your skin is literally keeping you together, forming a protective barrier that separates you from the outside world—and at the same time, it's busy moderating a two-way flow of water, oils, nutrients, and metabolic waste to keep your inner and outer environment in tune. Meanwhile, the skin is also monitoring what's happening with your immune system, protecting you from all sorts of problematic microbes and maintaining a microclimate that helps nurture beneficial bacteria that you need to stay healthy. And it's working full-time to keep your body temperature stable and provide information about what's going on in the world around you, interpreting sensations of heat, cold, pressure, pain, and touch.

1

Considering everything the skin does to keep us thriving, it's not a bad idea to give a little love back! Keeping skin nourished, toned, and moisturized doesn't just make it look good, it also helps your skin stay fit and healthy so it can continue doing all of its many important jobs.

Unfortunately, it's all too easy to judge our skin harshly; compared to an impossibly idealized, picture-perfect version of radiant, "healthy" skin (which usually comes from a bottle or a photo retouch!), it's easy to feel like we're too lumpy, bumpy, oily, or dry. We might feel too light, too dark, too pink, or too brown—anything except just right.

Homemade botanical skin care is one way to say thank you to the skin you're in, while also giving yourself some positive attention. When you're smoothing on skin-soothing cream, rubbing salve into tired feet, or soaking in a hot herbal bath at the end of a long day, you can choose to affirm the beauty, strength, and capacity of your incredible skin. And by caring for the skin in some very practical ways, you can keep it in top shape, so you can look and feel your best from the outside in!

In this book, we've captured many of our favorite tried-and-tested skin care recipes. We hope this resource will become a go-to in your household. Whether you're looking for a rich cream to pamper your face, a soothing salve for minor first aid, or topical support for a chronic skin condition, we've got something for you here. By the time you work your way through this recipe collection, you'll have a full cupboard of incredible skin care products to share with your friends and family—and maybe even your pets and neighbors, too!

We've designed this book to stand on its own, but it also serves as a companion to the **Herbal Academy's Botanical Skin Care Course.** This online program is packed with detailed information about the structure and function of the skin, nutrition and botanical support for chronic skin conditions, simple herbal first aid for acute skin issues, and information about Ayurveda and Chinese medicine for skin health. If this book inspires you, you may want to make the Botanical Skin Care Course the next stop on your journey into herbal skin care!

# Choosing Ingredients

The recipes in this book include a wide variety of ingredients—some you will likely be familiar with and some may be new to you. Because you might find yourself faced with making a choice between seven brands of essential oils, several types of shea butter, and a handful of natural preservative options, we've included some tips to get you started.

As a general rule, we recommend using organically cultivated or sustainably wild-harvested plant material for all herbal preparations, both for your own health and for the health of the plants and the planet! We also recommend using fresh, high-quality ingredients well within their shelf lives to facilitate a high-quality end product.

# HERBS

The quality and effectiveness of your skin care preparations will largely depend on the quality of the herbs and other ingredients you put into them.

As with everything, quality begins at the very start. How were the herbs grown? Were they grown organically and with care for the land? Were they harvested at the right time during their growth cycle and in the right season? Soil and water quality can make a great difference in how herbs grow, and even the time of day an herb is harvested can influence moisture and constituent levels.

After harvesting, were the herbs dried in a dark place, away from sunlight? Were they stored properly in airtight containers?

You may not be able to answer these questions completely if you have not grown, harvested, dried, and stored the herbs yourself. As a consumer, you must rely on your senses to determine the freshness of herbs; choosing herbs also requires a certain amount of trust in the reputation of farmers and retailers.

If you're shopping for herbs in your local natural foods co-op, herb shop, herbal CSA (community supported agriculture) group, or farmers market, a few things to look for are:

*A certified organic seal. Organically grown herbs are highly preferable to those sprayed with chemicals. Choosing organic is better for people, insects, ecosystems, soil, and surface water.*

*Sustainably wild-harvested. Wild plant populations can be decimated by over-harvesting.*

*Tightly sealed lid. Air degrades plant material and a poorly sealed container may allow moisture to seep inside (causing mold) or invasion from pantry pests.*

*Fresh color, scent, and taste. As dried plant matter ages, it starts to fade and be less aromatic. Look for bright, vivid herbs that smell and taste as you expect them to.*

Note that all of the herbal ingredients in the recipes throughout this book are dried herbs, unless otherwise noted.

## CARRIER OILS AND BUTTERS

Fixed or carrier oils should always be expeller-pressed, also known as cold-pressed or, particularly for olive oil, virgin. This means they have been mechanically extracted without the use of excess heat, which can damage the oils and promote the oxidation that causes oil to become rancid. Likewise, oils that are packaged in tightly sealed, dark-colored, and/or glass bottles are subjected to less ultraviolet radiation from sunlight, so they are likely to have a longer shelf life. Refrigerating oils will also extend shelf life.

Plant butters are available in a variety of forms: refined, unrefined, deodorized, and whitened. In some cases, the form that you choose will affect the consistency of your end product. While many of us tend to choose unrefined ingredients, refined, whitened, deodorized shea butter usually yields a lighter, fluffier, less oily product than the unrefined yellow shea butter, and it also emulsifies more easily—refined shea butter blends with the water-soluble ingredients in creams more readily than unrefined shea butter. The lighter consistency is preferred by many skin types, especially combination and oily skin. Additionally, the ease in emulsifying may be preferable for beginning product makers while honing techniques for making body butter and cream recipes. Nilotica shea butter is also an option for a light and fluffy cream or body butter; a subspecies of the better known *Vitellaria paradoxa* shea, nilotica is virtually scentless, even in its unrefined form, and is buttery soft.

A common-sense safety note on the use of oils and butters: those with food or plant allergies should avoid oils extracted from those plants—if eating mangoes makes your lips itch and burn, you may need to avoid mango butter in your skin products, too! It's always smart to do a skin patch test before using any new ingredients on your skin, particularly if you have other allergies or sensitivities.

When shopping for carrier oils and butters, remember to choose brands that invest in sustainable sourcing and fair-trade practices.

# BEESWAX ALTERNATIVES

If you would like to avoid using beeswax in your skin care products, you have a couple of options for beeswax substitutes. One option is emulsifying wax, which is a blend of fatty acids (e.g., cetearyl alcohol and glyceryl stearate) and detergents (e.g., polysorbate 60) that acts as an effective emulsifier and thickener. Emulsifying wax can add greater consistency, texture, thickness, and stabilization to topical applications compared to beeswax, with a less greasy finish and feel. Some emulsifying waxes are plant-derived and contain only relatively benign ingredients, but the trouble is that they may not be clearly labeled, so you don't always know what you're getting.

Plant-based waxes provide another alternative to beeswax; these can be derived from soybeans (soy wax), sunflower seeds (sunflower wax), palm trees (carnauba wax), or candelilla shrubs (candelilla wax). However, be aware that there may be sustainability concerns with both candelilla and carnauba wax, and soy wax is generally derived from non-organic, genetically modified soy, so do your research before buying.

If a recipe calls for beeswax and you'd like to replace it with a plant-based wax, you'll need to adjust your recipes to account for their differences in melting point and consistency:

*Candelilla and carnauba waxes:* Candelilla and carnauba waxes are very hard waxes. Therefore, if a recipe calls for beeswax and you'd like to use candelilla or carnauba wax instead, use ½ to ¾ of the amount called for in the recipe. So if your recipe calls for 10 grams of beeswax, use 5-7 grams of candelilla wax (Berry, 2016). And work fast, since these waxes harden twice as fast as beeswax!

*Sunflower wax:* Sunflower wax is even harder than candelilla wax; use about ⅓ of the amount of beeswax called for in the recipe. If your recipe calls for 10 grams of beeswax, use 2-4 grams of sunflower wax (Berry, 2016).

*Soy wax:* Soy wax is similar to beeswax in thickness and hardening time. Therefore, equal amounts can be substituted for beeswax.

## ESSENTIAL OILS

There are many conflicting opinions on the proper use of essential oils and the confusion is confounded by the many factors that come into play, including identification of exact plant species and chemotype, the method of extraction, the grade of oils used, and contaminants that may be present in the oil. Some skin experts avoid essential oils altogether, because many contain components that either are or can become irritating or sensitizing, and you'll see that many of our recipes include them as an optional ingredient. The high concentration of these volatile compounds and their potential for skin sensitization and irritation is a concern whether or not the oils are labeled with "certified" grades.

Although you may see essential oils marketed as "therapeutic grade" or "cosmetic grade," these terms don't have much meaning since there is no generally accepted grade or certification system for essential oils. Instead, aromatherapy experts recommend that you seek out brands that provide complete information about purity and quality testing; certified organic or biodynamic oils may provide excellent quality and minimize the possibility of contaminants.

When applying essential oils to the skin, they should always be diluted in a safe carrier, such as oil, thick aloe (*Aloe vera*) leaf gel, castile soap, or a dispersing agent such as Solubol. Water, alcohol, glycerin, vinegar, and hydrosol are not considered safe carriers for essential oils, as they do not effectively disperse the essential oils in the carrier.

It's best to conduct a patch test before applying essential oils that are new to your skin. Certain essential oils, especially some cold-pressed or expressed citrus oils, may be phototoxic upon exposure to sunlight. Extra caution is required when using essential oils around children, especially peppermint (*Mentha x piperita*) and eucalyptus (*Eucalyptus* spp.), and essential oils should be kept out of reach of both children and pets.

Keep all oil bottles tightly closed, cool, and away from direct sunlight.

## PLANT-DERIVED COMMERCIAL PRESERVATIVES

Some of the recipes in this book include the optional use of a natural preservative to extend shelf life. There are several options for plant-derived (non-synthetic) preservatives for body care products. These are natural, in that they are derived from plants, but they do need to be purchased from a commercial manufacturer—they're not something you can cook up in your kitchen at home!

These types of natural commercial preservatives have all been shown to help inhibit microbial growth, so they're particularly useful in lotions and creams where water (or watery liquids like hydrosols) have been included.

Preservatives that come from fermented sources may seem counterintuitive. After all, the point of a preservative is to minimize the risk of microbial growth, so adding an agent derived from bacteria might not make sense at first. However, there are several commercial preservatives, sold under the trade names of Leucidal® Liquid SF and Natapres™, that consist of peptides from fermented radishes.

PhytoCide is another type of natural preservative, derived from naturally occurring phytonutrients like caffeic, caprylic, and lauric acids, propanediol, potassium sorbate, and salicylates found in foods and botanicals such as aspen bark, coconut, corn, and elderberry.

Most commercial preservatives are available in several different formulations that have slightly different applications; for example, some may only be ideal for use in opaque creams, while some others have additional moisturizing or skin-conditioning benefits. Both Leucidal® Liquid SF and Natapres™ are approved through ECOCERT, an organic certification organization, so they can even be used in certified organic products.

If you choose to include a preservative, be sure to pay close attention to the manufacturer's instructions for use; these preservatives are sometimes only effective when added below a certain temperature and within a specific pH range, and need to be used at the concentration range recommended by the manufacturer—otherwise they may not fully preserve your homemade products.

It's easy enough to calculate how much preservative you need to use. Take a look at the label of the preservative you plan to use; it should list a suggested concentration range. This usually refers to concentration by weight, so if you're using a recipe that relies on volume measurements, you'll need to do a simple conversion:

1. Measure volume of each ingredient needed for the recipe, weighing each individually as well (in either grams or ounces); record the weight on the recipe for future use.

2. Add the weight of all ingredients to find the finished product weight.

3. Multiply by the suggested concentration in weight to determine the weight of preservative needed:

$$\text{Finished Product Weight} \times \text{Desired Preservative Concentration (as a decimal)} = \text{Weight of Preservative}$$

Example: Say the finished product weight of a batch of herbal cream is 200 g. The documentation for the preservative you want to use suggests a range of 2-4% by weight, and you determine that 2% is sufficient for your needs.

The total amount of preservative needed would be:

$$200 \text{ g} \times 0.02 = 4 \text{ g preservative}$$

In addition to following manufacturer recommendations, note that to be absolutely certain that microbial growth is inhibited, lab testing is required.

If you opt not to use a preservative in creams and lotions, be sure to make them in small batches that can be used within 1-2 weeks and always store in the refrigerator.

## ALOE

Skin care recipes may call for either aloe juice or aloe gel; both are cooling and anti-inflammatory, though aloe gel is generally more concentrated, and consequently may be a more effective humectant. If you're purchasing commercial aloe gel, make sure to get 100% aloe gel, and check the label for any of the preservatives or other synthetic ingredients you're trying to avoid!

## HONEY

Bees work very hard to produce honey. While honey has been a food and skin care product for humans for millennia, our impact on the environment means that we cannot take it—or honeybees—for granted. With respect for bees and ecology in mind, choose local, humanely gathered honey and beeswax from small-scale beekeeping operations whenever possible. Raw honey should be sought out for skin care preparations, since pasteurized honey may lose many of its antimicrobial benefits.

# Safety Tips

Common-sense safety tips to ensure your botanical skin care journey is a safe and happy one include conducting patch tests for any new-to-you ingredients, properly diluting essential oils, and checking in with your medical care provider if you are pregnant and/or nursing before using products with essential oils. In addition, always use caution when using oil-containing products in the tub or shower, as surfaces may become slippery.

We suggest wearing a dust mask when blending finely ground herbal powders and clays, as well as when working with activated charcoal powder.

If working with lye in soapmaking, there are a few very specific precautions to follow:

*Use only stainless steel equipment, as lye will react with other metals.*

*Make sure you use only 100% pure lye (sodium hydroxide) crystals, rather than liquid, and that lye isn't contaminated with any debris.*

*Wear appropriate safety gear including long-sleeved clothing, gloves, and safety goggles. Wear a charcoal mask (a cloth mask will not block the fumes, which must not be breathed in).*

*Mix lye and water (preferably distilled) outdoors. It is not advisable to mix indoors, even with an exhaust fan.*

*Always add lye to water—water should never be added to lye.*

*When cleaning up after making a batch of soap, wear protective gloves and clean all equipment in hot soapy water—the soap left on equipment will still be caustic!*

In general, using clean equipment is good practice for minimizing contamination and microbial growth and proliferation. Because microbial contamination is so common in lotions, creams, and other water-containing products, all supplies should be clean and sanitized when making these preparations, and we also suggest using distilled water and, if desired, a natural preservative. When making butter- and oil-based products, supplies should not only be clean and sanitized, but also completely dry. Use heat-safe bowls and jars when creating a makeshift double boiler, and make sure water doesn't splash into your double boiler when heating oils, butters, and waxes.

Use manufacturer's safety instructions when using blenders, mixers, and other kitchen equipment. Unplug your blender after blending and before stirring contents with a spoon, and never insert metal utensils into a working blender.

# Basic Tutorials

In this section, you will find tutorials for some basic herbal preparations you'll need to know how to make in order to complete the recipes in the course. Any additional herbal preparations you'll be making are described within the recipes themselves.

## *HOW TO MAKE AN HERB-INFUSED VINEGAR*

Herbal vinegars can be prepared using a very simple folk method that doesn't require measurement or a calculated weight-to-volume ratio. The folk method described below is perfect for topical preparations and simple, food-like tonics.

You can use either fresh or dry herbs to create an herbal vinegar, although dry herbs are often preferred because they don't introduce any extra water into your extract, which means an herbal vinegar made with dried plant material is likely to remain shelf stable for longer.

Raw apple cider vinegar is frequently used in herbal preparations, whether they're meant for the skin or for consumption. Although you can use other types of vinegar, these may not have the benefits found in apple cider vinegar. And it's quite easy to get unpasteurized, organic apple cider vinegar that doesn't contain any added ingredients, coloring, or preservatives and doesn't break the bank!

### HERB-INFUSED VINEGAR SUPPLIES

O   Clean, dry glass jar

O   Natural waxed paper and metal lid or plastic lid

O   Jelly bag, cheesecloth, or fine mesh sieve

O   Your herb and vinegar of choice (unpasteurized apple cider vinegar is recommended)

# HERB-INFUSED VINEGAR DIRECTIONS

1   Chop or crush the herbs. If you're using fresh herbs, use them as fresh as possible, and chop them just before using. If using dried herbs, crush them by hand or in a mortar and pestle just before using.

2   Loosely fill a clean, dry jar with prepared herb.

3   Pour apple cider vinegar over the herb, ensuring that the vinegar is covering the herb by at least 1 inch.

4   Place a square piece of natural waxed paper on top of the jar, then seal the jar with a lid (this protects the extract from any chemical coating that may be on the lid).

5   Cap tightly and give a shake to ensure that the herb and menstruum are thoroughly mixed.

6   Label the jar, store in a cool, dark location, and visit every 1-3 days, giving the jar a shake. Add a bit more vinegar if needed to keep herbs covered after they initially absorb some of the vinegar.

7   Let macerate for 4-6 weeks.

8   Line a wire strainer with a few layers of cheesecloth, or simply place the cheesecloth within a funnel placed in the mouth of a jar, and decant the mixture.

9   Strain the mixture through the cheesecloth and with clean, dry hands, gather the cloth up and squeeze strongly, squeezing as much liquid from the herbs as possible.

10  Transfer the liquid into a clean glass jar or bottle using a funnel.

11  Label with the date and ingredients, and store in a cool, dark place.

It's best to store all vinegar, herb-infused or not, out of direct light and in a well-sealed bottle. Exposure to air, heat, and light will cause oxidation that affects flavor and can reduce shelf life.

# HOW TO MAKE AN HERB-INFUSED OIL

There are several different methods you can use to prepare an herbal oil; in the following tutorial, we'll present both a very simple warm infusion method and a heated method using a saucepan or slow cooker. The instructions below are based on the folk method of making infused oil, which means you will eyeball the amounts and not measure or weigh. If you are more comfortable using measurements, the ratio is approximately 30 grams (1 oz) of dried herb to 355 mL (12 fl oz) of oil.

Herbal oils are less stable than other herbal preparations such as tinctures and vinegar extracts. Oils can more easily oxidize or become rancid, and they can even develop mold or bacterial growth. Adding water to oil is one of the things that makes it more prone to spoilage—be sure not to wash the herb or use a wet jar or wet spoon for mixing. Because of this, infused oils are most often made with dried herbs to eliminate the potential bacterial contamination, mold, and spoilage that may result when water is introduced to oil. However, some herbs are best infused fresh, such as St. John's wort (*Hypericum perforatum*) aerial parts, arnica (*Arnica* spp.) flower, gotu kola (*Centella asiatica*) leaf, and violet (*Viola* spp.) aerial parts, so we also include some tips for infusing fresh plant material safely.

Most carrier oils can be used to make an herb-infused oil. We suggest avoiding argan oil and rosehip seed oil if using the heated method of oil infusion—both of these oils are easily oxidized. When making a coconut oil infusion, melt the oil in a double boiler before infusing.

## HERB-INFUSED OIL SUPPLIES

O Saucepan or crock pot (optional)

O Heat-safe glass jar

O A large glass measuring cup or bowl with a spout

O Cheesecloth or jelly or nut milk bag

O Mesh strainer

O Dry, clean glass jars and lids for storage

O Marker and label(s)

# WARM OIL INFUSION DIRECTIONS

1   Grind dried herbs in a mortar and pestle or break them up in your clean hands to produce smaller pieces.

2   Fill a clean, dry glass jar half full with dried herbs.

3   Pour room-temperature oil over dried herbs in the jar, nearly to the top, making sure herbs are completely covered and oil is at least I inch above the top of the herbs. Use a clean, dry spoon or chopstick to mix thoroughly so that all herb surfaces are coated and no air bubbles remain.

4   Place a square piece of natural waxed paper on top of the jar, then seal the jar with a lid (this protects the herbal oil from any chemical coating that may be on the lid).

5   Roll the jar back and forth in your hands to continue to thoroughly mix the herb and oil, focusing your intention for the infused oil.

6   Place the jar in a dark, warm spot, but not directly in the sunlight unless you are using a dark-colored glass bottle or jar or have placed the jar in a brown paper bag. Let macerate for 4-6 weeks. Every 1-3 days, roll the jar in your hands to help mix the contents and release the herb's constituents into the oil. Revisit your intention for this herbal preparation.

7   Decant the oil after 4-6 weeks. Place a cheesecloth-lined strainer inside a large bowl with a spout. Pour the contents from the jar into the strainer. With clean, dry hands, gather the ends of the cheesecloth together and squeeze the remaining oil from the herb into the bowl. You'll want to squeeze hard to get every last drop!

8   Pour the oil into a clean, dry glass jar, cap, and let it settle overnight or for a few days.

9   Strain the oil again, being careful to avoid pouring out any of the remaining herb particulates that have settled to the bottom of the jar.

10 Pour the oil into clean and dry glass bottle(s) or jar(s) (ideally dark-colored glass bottles/jars to protect from light) and add a couple drops of vitamin E oil, if desired, to slow down oxidation of the oil. Cap tightly.

11 Label jar(s) and store in a cool, dark place. Shelf life will depend on the carrier oil used, but for most oils will be 9 months to 1 year.

## HEATED OIL INFUSION DIRECTIONS

1 Seal the herb- and oil-filled heat-safe glass jar and place in a saucepan or crock pot that has been filled with 2-3 inches of water and place a few jar lids under the jar to protect the base. (Alternatively, use a double boiler or makeshift double boiler—see below.)

2 Heat on very low heat for 8 hours (or more), making sure oil does not get warmer than 120-140 degrees F (preferably 100-110 degrees F) and refilling water as necessary as it evaporates. When measuring the temperature of the oil, be sure not to introduce water into the oil jar!

3 Remove jar from saucepan and allow to cool.

4 Decant and bottle as above.

5 Label jar(s) and store in a cool, dark place.

For a makeshift double boiler, find a large pot or pan that will completely hold another, smaller pot. Place water in the larger pot. Pour oil and herbs into the smaller pot, and place inside the larger pot with the water. Be careful not to splash any water into the oil. Keep an eye on the water level and replace water as needed.

# TIPS FOR USING FRESH HERBS FOR INFUSED OILS

After harvesting, place herbs on a drying screen and let them wilt for at least 1 day to remove some of the moisture. Once wilted, finely chop herbs into small pieces on a cutting board (or crush in a mortar and pestle) and fill the jar about ⅔-¾ full with the herb, adding oil to cover at least 1 inch above the top of the herbs.

If using the warm infusion method, keep an eye on the oil throughout the infusion process to make sure the herb stays below the surface of the oil to avoid mold growth. Smell the oil at the start of the infusion process and throughout to note any changes that might indicate spoilage (e.g., a fermented, swampy, or musty smell).

The heated infusion method is ideal for fresh herbs, as some of the water left in the herbs will evaporate during the infusion process; simply leave the lid off the jar during the infusion process.

Because oil is less dense than water, any water released from the herb during the infusion process will sink to the bottom of the jar where it will mix with any herb particulates that have settled. When decanting, pour slowly, and keep a close eye on this layer of water so it does not mix with the oil; decant only the oil portion, and discard any water or oil that is in contact with the water. After decanting the first time, let it settle again for a couple of days and repeat the process before the final bottling.

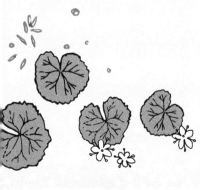

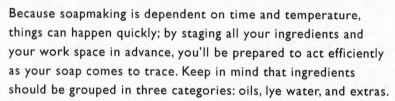

# HOW TO MAKE SOAP

Because soapmaking is dependent on time and temperature, things can happen quickly; by staging all your ingredients and your work space in advance, you'll be prepared to act efficiently as your soap comes to trace. Keep in mind that ingredients should be grouped in three categories: oils, lye water, and extras.

Once you've selected your recipe, gathered supplies, and completed any preliminary steps—for example, infusing herbs into oil or water—you're ready to begin!

## SOAP SUPPLIES

This is a basic list of equipment; as batches get more complicated, other tools will be needed. Note that stainless steel equipment is important because lye will react with other metals.

O Stainless steel pot: The deeper the better, even for smaller batches, to avoid splashing while blending.

O Large stainless steel spoon

O Scale that displays ounces to the tenths place (e.g., 7.2 ounces)

O Large bowl for measuring oils

O Plastic bowl for lye water: Preferably a dedicated bowl for mixing lye and water. Plastic is preferable because lye tends to stick to the bottom of a glass bowl, making it harder to incorporate; glass also takes longer to cool than plastic.

O Immersion blender: If you do not have an immersion blender, you can use a hand mixer or a whisk, but an immersion blender will help soap come to trace (thicken) faster. Ideally, your immersion blender will have a detachable stainless steel blade and shaft, but blenders with a plastic shaft or blade can also be used.

O Rubber spatula

O Thermometer: An inexpensive candy thermometer is fine.

O Soap mold

O   Mold liner like parchment paper or natural waxed paper for easy removal of soap; anything other than silicone soap molds will need to be lined.

O   Soap cutter: You can use a straight-edged knife or a flat stainless steel scraper or chopping tool; you can also buy a soap mold with sectional inserts so that you do not have to cut the soap by hand, or buy a soap cutting tool. Sectional inserts make it easy to have uniform soap sizes and shapes.

O   Towels or blankets to insulate the soap while it's in the mold. Soap can lose heat too quickly especially in cold winter months; insulating helps soap create more glycerin and ensure that the soap is not cooling down and slowing the saponification process too rapidly.

O   Small resealable bag for weighing lye (optional)

## SOAP DIRECTIONS

### STEP 1: PREPARE THE AREA AND SUPPLIES

A good household rule is that no one is allowed in the kitchen while you are making soap. You won't want children underfoot while bringing lye water in from the back porch or trying to quickly pour the soap batch before it sets up!

Cover the mold with parchment paper or a waxed paper liner, unless using a silicone mold that doesn't require a liner. (Tip: Use your finger to crease the paper in the shape of your mold. Turn curled paper over so that it curls downward, that way you won't have to use tape to keep it from slipping in the mold.)

### STEP 2: WEIGH INGREDIENTS

Soap ingredients are measured by weight, not volume; make sure your scale is set to the correct unit of measurement for your recipe.

Weigh all ingredients carefully. The smaller the batch, the more precise your measurements must be in order to avoid any problems.

Weigh all oils individually in a large bowl, then use a rubber spatula to scrape the oils into a large stainless steel pot.

Weigh water in a dedicated plastic container or glass bowl, and set aside.

Weigh lye crystals.

It can be helpful to weigh lye into a small zip top bag. This also acts as a reminder to not pour water into the lye, and instead pour lye into the water!

## STEP 3: COMBINE LYE AND WATER

Always complete this step outdoors, and wear gloves, eye protection, and a charcoal mask. This is very important.

Take your measured water, lye, and a stainless steel spoon outside, and set up on a flat, stable surface.

Pour all of the lye into the water and stir briefly to dissolve. It will only take a few seconds to dissolve, but will give off poisonous fumes for about a minute. Do not breathe the fumes or put your arms near them.

Allow the lye water to cool to 90-110 degrees F.

## STEP 4: MELT OILS

Once all oils, butters, and/or fats are weighed and added to the large stainless steel pot, gently heat them until they are melted and incorporated.

Cool oils to 90-110 degrees F.

## STEP 5: COMBINE OILS AND LYE WATER AND BRING TO TRACE

The trick to combining the oils and lye water is to do it when they are both between 90 and 110 degrees F. This can require a bit of juggling!

If the lye water cools too quickly, carefully place the bowl of lye water in a hot water bath. Alternatively, oils can be placed in a hot water bath or cold water bath to adjust temperatures so that the oils and lye water achieve the optimal temperature range at the same time. Because the lye water is more dangerous to work with, you may want to focus on adjusting the temperature of the oil mixture once the lye water is in the correct temperature range.

Next, pour the lye water into the oil mixture and blend thoroughly to emulsify, using an immersion blender. Once the mixture is well-combined and the saponification process begins, the soap batch will look creamy and will begin to thicken to trace. Once it reaches a light to medium trace, the soap is ready for extra ingredients or to pour into the mold.

## TRACE

*"Coming to trace"* is a term frequently used in soapmaking; it describes the beginning of the saponification reaction, in which the soap begins to visibly thicken. The term trace comes from the slight line or trace that can be seen when the soap that is beginning to thicken is drizzled over the top of the still-liquid soap. As the soap thickens, the trace line becomes thicker.

Soap recipes may describe trace as thin, medium, or thick in order to help you know when your soap is ready to pour. Certain design elements, such as layering or swirling, may rely on having a thicker or thinner trace.

Thin trace is not raised, but is a line that can be seen in the light as the soap is drizzled over the batch.

Medium trace is slightly thicker, with a thin raised line when drizzled over the top.

Thick trace is more like a waffle batter. This is perfect for layering different colors. If it begins to get more like pudding in consistency, then it will be more difficult to pour and work with in the mold.

Trace is a critical part of soapmaking, so be sure to watch closely.

If you do not have an immersion blender, you can use a stainless steel, plastic, or silicone hand mixer or whisk, but it will take longer to bring the soap to trace. Make sure the mixture has a uniform consistency in color and texture or there will be pockets of liquid in the soap.

## STEP 6: ADD EXTRA INGREDIENTS

Many extra ingredients, such as exfoliants, essential oils, and colorants, are added at trace.

After adding essential oils or other "extras," blend again to thoroughly combine everything.

This step doesn't need to be rushed, but always be aware of how fast the soap is setting up. If the recipe calls for many additional steps, such as dividing the batch, adding herbs and essential oils, and creating swirling techniques, you may need to work a little more quickly.

## STEP 7: POUR AND INSULATE

Pour soap into the prepared mold, scraping with a rubber spatula and smoothing the top if necessary.

Insulate lightly for 24 hours with towels (heavier in cooler winter temperatures) for an even, full gel and brighter colors. (Gel is a stage during saponification when the entire batch darkens and becomes almost translucent, only to later lighten significantly. This only occurs when enough heat is retained through insulation. Gelling produces harder soaps with brighter, creamier colors. Soap makers wanting whiter soaps try to avoid the gel stage with refrigeration during the first 24 hours in the mold.) Depending on the size and shape of your mold, it might make sense to put the mold of soap into a small shoebox to protect the soap, and then wrap the shoebox in towels.

## STEP 8: CUT AND CURE

After about 24 hours, check to see if the soap is ready to remove from the mold. It should be firm enough to remove and cut without dimpling or breaking.

Remove soap from the mold and cut.

Allow to cure for 4-6 weeks in a cool, dry location. During this time, the saponification process will continue and extra water will evaporate, producing a harder, long-lasting bar.

Make sure there's some air flow as your bars cure; completely sealed containers can trap in moisture and cause mold. If storing in a container like a plastic shoe box, leave the lid slightly open.

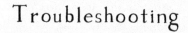

# Troubleshooting

When making topical preparations that contain oil, especially when oil is combined with a water-based ingredient, problems can arise for a number of reasons. Here are a few simple tips to minimize common oil-, salve-, lotion-, cream-, gel-, and soap-making issues.

## SALVES AND OILS

**Salves are an undesired consistency:** If you are unhappy with the consistency of your salve, you can always remelt it (using clean, dry equipment!) and add additional beeswax if your salve is too soft or additional oil if it is too hard.

**Salves/oils exposed to water:** If you forgot to use dry equipment or accidentally spilled water on your work area and salves or oil were exposed to water, your salve/oil is at risk of bacterial or fungal contamination and should be used immediately (or within 1-2 weeks in the refrigerator), and then discarded.

**Salves/oils have unidentified floating objects:** Sometimes, plant particulates or soil (or even bee parts from beeswax!) end up in your product. If plant material was fully dried before infusing in oil, it is unlikely that it will cause the product to spoil, but if you don't like the aesthetics of floaters, you can remelt the salve and strain it (or the oil) through a couple of layers of cheesecloth or a jelly or nut milk bag. (For very fine particles, you may need to use a coffee filter.)

**Salve/oil has an "off" smell:** Oils and salves are at risk of oxidation and spoilage. Salves or oils that smell fermented or rancid should be discarded—in the future, add a few drops of vitamin E oil to prevent oxidation, and make sure that all herbs and equipment are dry.

# CREAMS AND LOTIONS

**Lotion or cream is too thin:** If a lotion or cream is too thin, that's an indication that there is too much water relative to the amount of oil. This will require an adjustment to the water-to-oil ratio. It is difficult to thicken a watery lotion; however, the lotion may be salvageable if more oil is added. Be sure the oil and lotion are the same temperature, then add oil very slowly, as adding too much (or too quickly) may cause the lotion to separate.

**Lotion or cream is too thick:** If a lotion or cream is too thick, increase the amount of water-based ingredients in the recipe. Slowly drizzling more water-based liquid into the emulsifying lotion/cream during the blending process should thin it out. But remember, go slowly. You can add liquid, but you can't take it away.

**Lotion or cream is too greasy:** If a lotion or cream is too greasy, stir in tapioca starch or arrowroot powder by hand, ¼ teaspoon at a time with a whisk or spoon, until the mixture becomes smoother and less greasy. Instead of oils and butters that absorb into the skin slowly, such as coconut oil, olive oil, and cocoa butter, choose those that absorb more quickly, such as apricot or grapeseed oil.

**Separation in a lotion or cream:** If a lotion or cream has separated, this may be an indication that your water and oil ingredients weren't the same temperature when you combined them. This can be remedied by heating up your lotion or cream in a double boiler and stirring continually just until it liquifies. This process should not take long; don't allow the mixture to get so hot that it begins to steam. Remove the mixture from the heat and blend it again until it stabilizes, then store it in the refrigerator. Lotions and creams can also separate when exposed to hot temperatures. If it's hot outside (over 80 degrees F with high humidity), store your lotions and creams in the refrigerator.

**Mold in a lotion or cream:** If a cream or lotion has become moldy, this is a sign of microbial contamination at some point in the production process. (Individual jars of cream or lotion can also be contaminated during use, simply from bacteria on your fingers, and bacterial growth is not always visible.) To prevent microbial contamination, make sure any equipment used to make creams and lotions, including bowls, blenders, spatulas, storing jars, measuring spoons, and measuring cups, is clean, sanitized, and dry. A lotion or cream that becomes moldy or otherwise suspect should be discarded. To prevent microbial contamination in the future, in addition to meticulously clean equipment, consider adding a preservative to your next batch.

## GELS

**Temperature:** If your formula isn't thickening into a gel, or if the powdered hydrocolloid (e.g., xanthan gum, Irish moss, etc.) is not blending with the other ingredients in your formula, try warming up the formula either in a warm water bath, using heat-proof glassware, and stirring as you warm. Remember that the formula will continue to thicken as it cools, so you won't be able to gauge the final texture until it has cooled back to room temperature.

**Thickness:** Once your gel formula has cooled to room temperature, you may find that the consistency of the gel is not quite what you had in mind. If it is not thick enough, add more of your chosen hydrocolloid in small amounts until you achieve the desired thickness. If it is too thick, add more water, or your chosen water-based solvent, to loosen the thickness of the gel.

**Clumping:** When the hydrocolloid powder is first added to water, it has a tendency to clump together, even after blending the mixture thoroughly. Simply set the mixture aside and allow the hydrocolloid molecules the time they need to bond with the hydrogen, and then blend again. Repeat this process a few times until the powder has completely dissolved in the water.

**Emulsions:** Only blend oils into a gel formula once all water-based ingredients have been combined and the hydrocolloid has been added and completely dissolved.

## SOAPS

**Not coming to trace:** Recipes with liquid oils, castile or bastille recipes, soap that is too cold, or using too much water or not enough lye can cause soap to take longer to come to trace. Try to determine whether it is at light trace by drizzling some of the soap from the pot over the top of the batch with a large spoon. Look for a "trail" or line from the drizzle. Sometimes this is best seen with a light overhead. If you see the trail, then go ahead and pour into the mold and insulate. If the batch is too cold, gently reheat to 90-110 degrees F. Continue stirring to see if soap comes to trace, even for a couple hours if you are so inclined. If trace doesn't happen, or if mixture separates into oil and water, soap is likely unusable and should be discarded. Make sure to double check the ingredient amounts and temperatures next time!

**Coming to trace too fast:** Higher temperature can cause soap to come to trace too fast. This means that the soap is becoming thick very quickly and can make it difficult to add ingredients, layer, or swirl the soap. It can also cause soap to seize in the pot, meaning it will harden so fast that you are unable to scoop it into the mold. Fragrance oils and warming essential oils like cinnamon and clove can also speed trace. For future batches, combine oil and lye water at lower temperatures. Some batches can be salvaged by scooping into the mold and smoothing the top. If it hardens in the pot, hot-process it by placing the soap chunks in a crockpot on the lowest setting; cover with plastic wrap so that no moisture is lost (very important), and heat until the entire batch softens to a mashed potato-like consistency. Then, remove cover, stir, add essential oils if needed, and scoop into mold. This hot-processed soap is ready to use after it hardens—no extra cure time is needed.

**Hard, chalky soap that crumbles when cut:** This is a sign that too much lye was added. The high sodium hydroxide (lye) content in these bars produces an alkaline soap that may be caustic. Discard this soap and do not use.

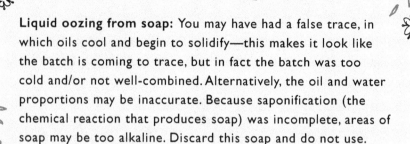

**Liquid oozing from soap:** You may have had a false trace, in which oils cool and begin to solidify—this makes it look like the batch is coming to trace, but in fact the batch was too cold and/or not well-combined. Alternatively, the oil and water proportions may be inaccurate. Because saponification (the chemical reaction that produces soap) was incomplete, areas of soap may be too alkaline. Discard this soap and do not use.

**Gel-like soap with bubbles or split on top:** This is the result of overheating. If the batch hardens after cutting and curing then it is fine to use. If it doesn't solidify with curing, you will need to hot-process.

**White powdery substance on top of soap:** This is known as soda ash, and is purely a cosmetic defect; the soap is perfectly fine to use. It's the result of contact between unsaponified lye and carbon dioxide in the air, so covering your soap with plastic wrap or curing in a closed plastic tub may help with future batches. To remove the ash, you can gently rub the top of the cured soap under running water (while wearing gloves), or use a potato peeler or knife to gently remove the top layer. If the soap also contains pockets of a white powdery substance throughout the soap, it is likely that an excess of lye was used, and thus this soap is caustic and should not be used.

# Let's Get Started!

In this introductory chapter we've included the basic information you'll need to choose ingredients, work with them safely, and troubleshoot as you experiment with the recipes in this book. If you're interested in furthering your understanding of botanical skin care beyond the hands-on creation and use of these recipes, **Herbal Academy's Botanical Skin Care Course** dives deep into the ways you can support your skin health both internally and externally. There is plenty here in this book to guide you down this path of discovery, so let's get started exploring this fun and fulfilling way of caring for our skin and wellness!

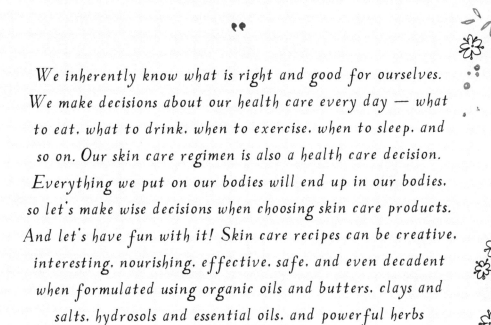

*We inherently know what is right and good for ourselves. We make decisions about our health care every day — what to eat, what to drink, when to exercise, when to sleep, and so on. Our skin care regimen is also a health care decision. Everything we put on our bodies will end up in our bodies, so let's make wise decisions when choosing skin care products. And let's have fun with it! Skin care recipes can be creative, interesting, nourishing, effective, safe, and even decadent when formulated using organic oils and butters, clays and salts, hydrosols and essential oils, and powerful herbs and herbal infusions.*

MARLENE ADELMANN, FOUNDER OF THE HERBAL ACADEMY

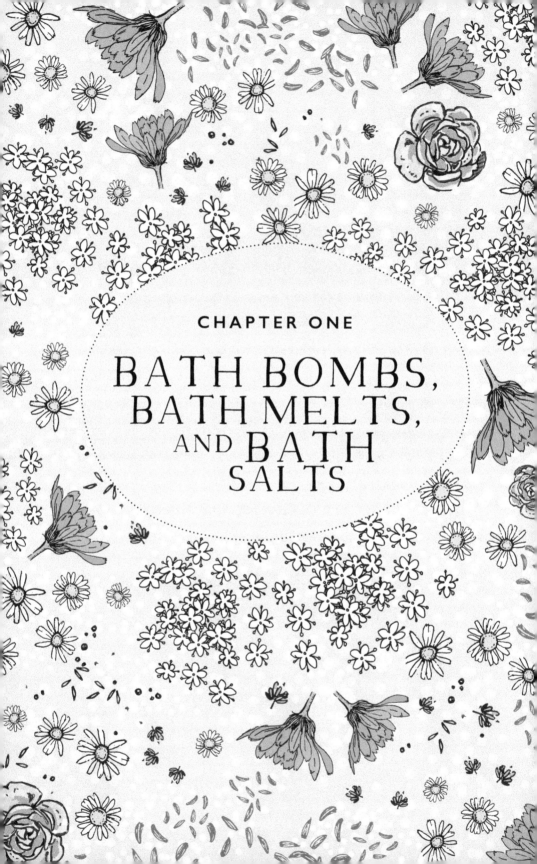

# CHAPTER ONE

# BATH BOMBS, BATH MELTS, AND BATH SALTS

# BATH BOMBS, BATH MELTS, AND BATH SALTS

What could be better than unwinding with a long,
hot soak in the tub? A bath with an herbal boost!
These bath bombs and melts are a fun and simple
way to turn an ordinary bath into a fizzy, silky, and
skin-soothing delight. Herbal bath salts give you the
relaxing and nourishing qualities of a mineral bath,
along with the aromatic benefits of herbs
and essential oils—an herbal hot spring
right in your tub!

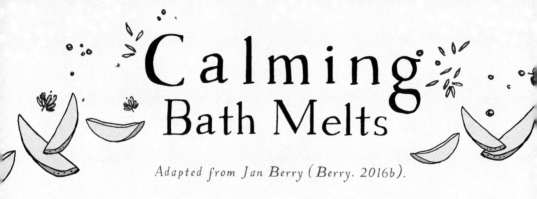

# Calming
## Bath Melts

*Adapted from Jan Berry (Berry. 2016b).*

## INGREDIENTS

3½ tbsp shea butter

3½ tbsp mango butter

½ tbsp ground magnesium chloride or magnesium sulfate (Epsom salt)

10-30 drops of lavender (*Lavandula* spp.) essential oil

———————

Let the emollient butters and subtle lavender scent soothe your senses.
A great pre-bedtime bath melt blend.

## DIRECTIONS

Gently heat shea and mango butters in a double boiler over low heat (or a glass or ceramic bowl or canning jar over a small saucepan of simmering water) until melted.

Remove from heat, add the magnesium chloride or Epsom salt, and stir to incorporate.

Allow to cool a bit before adding the essential oil, as heat evaporates essential oils.

Once the essential oils are incorporated, pour the combined ingredients into a silicone mold.

While the butters are still warm and in liquid form, clean up excess butter on your equipment with paper towels; once cool, the butters harden and become very tricky to remove.

Allow the bath melts to cool to room temperature before removing from the mold.

Store bath melts in an airtight glass jar in a cool, dark place for up to 1 year (in hot climates, store in the refrigerator).

Add 1 bath melt to the tub when you begin to draw the hot bathwater.

Use caution when leaving the tub as the melts will make the bathtub slippery, and remember to wipe down the tub afterwards!

# Basic
# BATH BOMBS

*Adapted from Katie Wells (Wells. 2019b).*

## INGREDIENTS

1 cup baking soda

½ cup citric acid

½ cup sea salt
or Epsom salt

½ cup cornstarch

2 tbsp (1 fl oz)
carrier oil (e.g., herb-
infused oil, sea buckthorn
oil, rosehip seed oil,
evening primrose oil)

1-2 tbsp (0.5-1 fl oz)
liquid (e.g., aloe
(*Aloe vera*) leaf juice,
hydrosol, tincture)

30-40 drops essential oil
(optional)

1 tsp powdered herb(s)
(optional)

---

You can use this
recipe as a basic
framework and plug
herbal ingredients
into the oil and
liquid portions.

## DIRECTIONS

In a large bowl, combine all dry ingredients
and mix well until combined.

In a small bowl, combine all wet ingredients.

Slowly add the wet ingredients to the large bowl
of dry ingredients, mixing by hand.

You have achieved bath bomb texture once
all combined ingredients hold together without
crumbling when squeezed. If the combined
ingredients are still a bit crumbly, add more
liquid until all ingredients hold together well:
use a spray bottle to add more liquid until you
reach a perfect consistency.

Quickly push the combined mixture into the molds
(a muffin tin works fine) or shape into balls with
your hands. Press firmly and leave for 3-4 hours
or until hardened. The mixture will expand as it
dries: you can continue to shape the balls or press
the material into the mold as it dries to keep it
from expanding too much.

Once dry, remove from the mold if used (a hard
whack on the countertop will pop them out of
the upside-down muffin tin), then let cure for
1 week. Once completely dry, transfer to an
airtight container and label.

Store in a cool, dark place for
up to 6 months.

# Wound-Soothing Bath Melts

*Adapted from Jan Berry (Berry, 2016b).*

Use these bath melts to speed the healing of topical wounds as well as to ease inflammation and pain.

## INGREDIENTS

### STEP 1

½ cup shea butter

½ cup cocoa butter

¾ cup calendula (*Calendula officinalis*) flower

### STEP 2

7 tbsp shea and cocoa butter infused with calendula (*Calendula officinalis*) flower

5 drops yarrow (*Achillea millefolium*) essential oil

5 drops chamomile (*Matricaria chamomilla*) essential oil

5 drops frankincense (*Boswellia* spp.) essential oil, sustainably sourced

## DIRECTIONS

### STEP 1

Use a coffee grinder to grind up the dried calendula flowers.

Make the calendula-infused shea and cocoa butters using the instructions in the herb-infused oil tutorial.

## STEP 2

If needed, gently heat the calendula-infused butter in a double boiler over low heat (or a glass or ceramic bowl or canning jar over a small saucepan of simmering water) until melted.

Allow to cool a bit before adding the essential oil, as heat evaporates essential oils.

Once the essential oils are incorporated, pour the combined ingredients into a silicone mold.

While the butters are still warm and in liquid form, clean up excess butter on your equipment with paper towels; once cool, the butters harden and become very tricky to remove.

Allow the bath melts to cool to room temperature before removing from the mold.

Store bath melts in an airtight glass jar in a cool, dark place for up to 1 year (in hot climates, store in the refrigerator).

Add 1 bath melt to the tub when you begin to draw the hot bathwater.

Use caution when leaving the tub as the melts will make the bathtub slippery, and remember to wipe down the tub afterwards!

# Skin-Soothing
## BATH SALTS

### INGREDIENTS

¾ cup sea salt

¾ cup baking soda

¾ cup coarsely to finely powdered oatmeal

½ cup elder (*Sambucus canadensis* or *S. nigra*) flower

½ cup chamomile (*Matricaria chamomilla*) flower

### DIRECTIONS

Pour all ingredients into a clean, dry bowl; stir to combine.

Store in a labeled glass jar in a cool, dry place.

Use one or two handfuls of the blend per bath.

Place in a muslin bag and hang over the faucet
while the water is running.

Baking soda baths and oatmeal baths are both commonly
used to calm irritated skin—together with the addition
of elderflower, which has a long history of use for skin
conditions such as eczema and psoriasis, and anti-
inflammatory chamomile, these bath salts offer the
ultimate treat for itchy or irritated skin.

# ⋛ Simplest ⋚
# BATH SALTS

These no-mess, no-frills, simple salts can be made in less than 1 minute; they're virtually indestructible, won't stain or clog your bathtub, and can be infinitely customized with essential oils. And if you're lacking a bathtub, they make for a wonderfully relaxing foot soak!

## INGREDIENTS

2 cups Epsom salt

1 cup sea salt

½ cup baking soda

2 tbsp (1 fl oz) sweet almond, grapeseed, or olive oil

20 drops lavender (*Lavandula* spp.) or other essential oil of your choice

## DIRECTIONS

Combine salts and baking soda and mix thoroughly.

To make sure essential oil stays diluted and dispersed when adding salts to bathwater, combine essential oil with oil before adding to the salt mixture. Stir thoroughly.

Place mixture in a glass jar, label, and store in a cool, dark place for 6–12 months.

Use 1–2 cups per bath, or ⅛ –¼ cup for a foot bath.

# Flowery
## BATH SALTS

### INGREDIENTS

1 cup Epsom salt

1 cup sea salt or pink Himalayan salt

½ cup baking soda

½ cup rose (*Rosa* spp.) petal or bud

½ cup lavender (*Lavandula* spp.) flower bud

½ cup calendula (*Calendula officinalis*) flower

½ cup tulsi (*Ocimum tenuiflorum*) aerial parts

### DIRECTIONS

Combine all ingredients in a large bowl and mix thoroughly.

Place mixture into a glass jar, label, and store in a cool, dark place for 12–18 months.

Use 1–2 handfuls of salt per bath. Before draining, place a sink/bath strainer over the drain to catch the herb material. Alternatively, place salts in a muslin bag and hang over the faucet while filling the bath.

This classic bath salt recipe combines the rejuvenation of a salt soak with the beauty and calm of a cottage garden.

# Antifungal
## BATH SALTS

Using herbs for fungal infection of the skin or nails doesn't have to be a chore! Whip up this batch of antifungal bath salts, and draw yourself a soothing (and supporting!) full-body, foot, or hand bath.

### INGREDIENTS

1½ cups baking soda

½ cup sea salt

½ cup (4 fl oz) tamanu or fractionated coconut oil

30 drops total of a combination of:

tea tree (*Melaleuca alternifolia*) essential oil,
lavender (*Lavandula* spp.) essential oil,
basil (*Ocimum basilicum*) essential oil,
and/or coriander (*Coriandrum sativum*) essential oil

### DIRECTIONS

Pour baking soda and salt into a clean, dry bowl.

To make sure essential oil stays diluted and dispersed when adding salts to bathwater, combine essential oil with oil before adding to the salt. Stir thoroughly.

Place mixture into a glass jar, label, and store in a cool, dark place for 6-12 months.

Add 1-2 handfuls of salt per bath.

# NOURISHING MILK BATH SALTS

Herb-infused milk baths are nourishing and luxurious, and leave skin feeling soft and supple. Skip the step of infusing herbs in milk by using powdered milk in this quick-to-put-together bath salt blend!

*INGREDIENTS*

2 cups Epsom salt

1 cup powdered milk

¼ cup powdered oats

¼ cup calendula (*Calendula officinalis*) flower powder

¼ cup comfrey (*Symphytum officinale*) leaf powder

¼ cup lavender (*Lavandula* spp.) flower bud powder

*DIRECTIONS*

Pour all ingredients into a clean, dry bowl.

Place mixture into a glass jar for storage, label, and store in a cool, dark place for 6–12 months.

Add 1–2 handfuls of salt per bath.

# CLEARING BATH SALTS

These aromatic bath salts are clearing to the respiratory system. Not for use with children under the age of 6 due to the eucalyptus and peppermint essential oil component.

*INGREDIENTS*

1 cup Epsom salt

¾ cup sea salt

¼ cup baking soda

½ cup (4 fl oz) sweet almond oil

8 drops eucalyptus (*Eucalyptus* spp.) essential oil

8 drops balsam fir (*Abies balsamea*) essential oil

6 drops peppermint (*Mentha x piperita*) essential oil

*DIRECTIONS*

Pour baking soda and salts into a clean, dry bowl.

To make sure essential oil stays diluted and dispersed when adding salts to bathwater, combine essential oil with sweet almond oil before adding to the salt mixture. Stir thoroughly.

Place mixture into a glass jar, label, and store in a cool, dark place for 6–12 months.

Add 1–2 handfuls of salt per bath.

# Evergreen Forest
## BATH SALTS

Luxurious Dead Sea salt combines with the grounding and antimicrobial nature of pine needles for a relaxing bath. Fir or spruce needles can be substituted.

## INGREDIENTS

3 cups Dead Sea salt
(or any sea salt)

½ cup pine (*Pinus* spp.) needle, finely chopped

½ cup juniper
(*Juniperus communis*) berry, crushed

2 tbsp (1 fl oz) sweet almond, grapeseed, or olive oil

6 drops fir (*Abies balsamea*) essential oil (optional)

6 drops Virginia cedarwood (*Juniperus virginiana*) essential oil (optional)

## DIRECTIONS

Combine salt, pine needles, and juniper berries in a medium-sized bowl and mix thoroughly.

To make sure essential oil stays diluted and dispersed when adding salts to bathwater, combine essential oil with oil before adding to the salt mixture. Stir thoroughly.

Place mixture into a glass jar, label, and store in a cool, dark place for 6-12 months.

Use 1-2 handfuls of salt per bath. Before draining, place a sink/bath strainer over the drain to catch the herb material. Alternatively, place salts in a muslin bag and hang over the faucet while filling the bath.

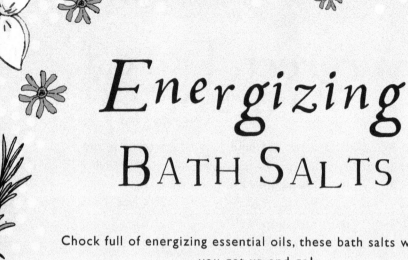

# Energizing
# Bath Salts

Chock full of energizing essential oils, these bath salts will help you get up and go!

## INGREDIENTS

1 cup sea salt

¼ cup (2 fl oz) sweet almond oil

4 drops rosemary (*Rosmarinus officinalis*) essential oil

3 drops Texas cedarwood (*Juniperus mexicana*) essential oil

2 drops juniper (*Juniperus communis*) essential oil

2 drops sweet orange (*Citrus x sinensis*) essential oil

## DIRECTIONS

Pour sea salt into a clean, dry bowl.

To make sure essential oil stays diluted and dispersed when adding salts to bathwater, combine essential oil with sweet almond oil before adding to the salt. Stir thoroughly.

Place mixture into a glass jar, label, and store in a cool, dark place for 6-12 months.

Add 1-2 handfuls of salt per bath.

# Lovely Lavender Bath Bombs

*Adapted from Mountain Rose Herbs (Mountain Rose Herbs. 2011).*

## INGREDIENTS

1 cup baking soda

½ cup citric acid

½ cup Epsom salt

1 tsp jojoba oil

15 drops lavender (*Lavandula* spp.) essential oil

1 tbsp (0.5 fl oz) lavender (*Lavandula* spp.) hydrosol

¼ cup lavender (*Lavandula* spp.) flower bud

## DIRECTIONS

Combine baking soda, citric acid, and Epsom salt in a medium-sized bowl and mix thoroughly.

In a small bowl, combine jojoba oil and lavender essential oil, stirring thoroughly. Add to salts and stir to combine.

Add lavender hydrosol and stir to combine: mixture should be moist enough to hold together when squeezed in your hand. Note that adding too much hydrosol will cause the mixture to puff up and expand during drying, so limit to 1 tablespoon if possible.

Add lavender buds and stir to combine.

Create bath bombs by shaping into a ball with your hands and packing thoroughly.

Let dry for 3-4 hours, then let cure for 1 week. Once completely dry, transfer to an airtight container and label. Store in a cool, dark place for up to 6 months.

Use 1-2 bombs per bath, depending on size. Place a strainer over drain when draining water to catch the lavender buds!

**Fun to make and use, these calming bath bombs are bursting with skin-friendly lavender.**

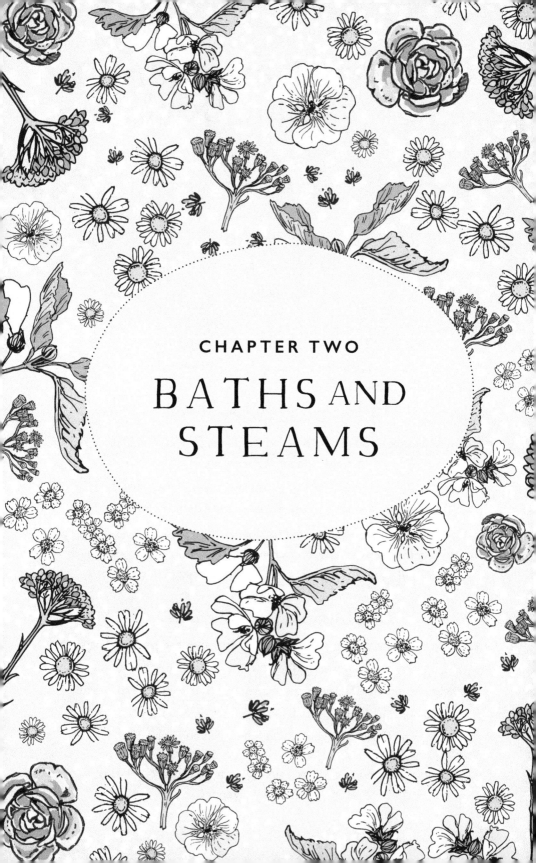

CHAPTER TWO

# BATHS AND STEAMS

# BATHS AND STEAMS

Herbal baths and steams offer us a chance to truly immerse ourselves in herbs! Soaking in a hot and beautifully scented herbal bath is certainly a treat for the senses, and a wonderful self-care ritual— but it's also an effective way to take advantage of the properties of many herbs, which can be delivered to the body either by inhalation or by absorption through the skin.

If you don't have access to a bathtub, you can still take advantage of many of the benefits of herbal bathing by using hand or foot soaks, sitz baths, and simple herbal steams.

# Herbal
# FACIAL STEAM

## INGREDIENTS

2 tbsp chamomile (*Matricaria chamomilla*) flower

2 tbsp lavender (*Lavandula* spp.) flower bud

2 tbsp yarrow (*Achillea millefolium*) aerial parts

2 tbsp thyme (*Thymus vulgaris*) aerial parts

2 quarts (64 fl oz) water

## DIRECTIONS

Combine herbs in a wide glass or ceramic bowl.

Heat water to boiling, then pour over herbs.

Sit comfortably with face positioned
10 inches from the bowl – close enough to feel the steam,
but not so close as to be burned by it.

Cover head with a towel, creating a tent
over your head and the bowl.

Steam face for approximately 5 minutes.

Splash cool water on face and gently pat dry with a clean towel.

An herbal steam with antimicrobial and antiseptic herbs can be a
lovely way to pamper and support irritated, acne-prone skin.

# Relaxing Hydrosol
## BATH BLEND

This recipe is the perfect aromatherapeutic treat for individuals who are sensitive to essential oils—skip the essential oil-rich bath salts and balms, and add this hydrosol blend to bathwater! (We think you essential oil lovers out there will love this one, too!)

### INGREDIENTS

½ cup (4 fl oz) neroli (*Citrus x aurantium*) hydrosol

¼ cup (2 fl oz) lemon balm (*Melissa officinalis*) hydrosol

¼ cup (2 fl oz) lemon verbena (*Aloysia citriodora*) hydrosol

### DIRECTIONS

Combine hydrosols in an 8-ounce glass bottle.

Label, and store in a cool, dark place or refrigerator for up to 6 months.

Add 2-3 tablespoons to bathwater.

# Seaweed & Oat
## BATH

### INGREDIENTS

¼ cup rolled oats

¼ cup dried seaweed, any type

*(kelp and bladderwrack work well)*

### DIRECTIONS

Combine oats and seaweed in a muslin bag,
or wrap up in a cheesecloth bundle and knot it at the top.
(This will keep the herbs from clogging up your drain!)

Bring a pot of water to a boil and add the bundle.

Cover and steep for 30 minutes.

Add the hot water with the bundle to your bath.
Soak and enjoy!

Follow with moisturizer.

When you need only the most soothing, cooling, and—let's
admit it—ever-so-slimy herbs to ease your sunburned,
irritated, and inflamed skin, this bath has your back.
(Along with your arms, legs, and any other part of you
that has the itchy-burnies!)

# After-Sun
# Vinegar Bath

## INGREDIENTS

4 cups (32 fl oz) apple cider vinegar

1 cup rose (*Rosa* spp.) petal

½ cup peppermint (*Mentha* x *piperita*) leaf

½ cup marshmallow (*Althaea officinalis*) root

¼ cup coriander (*Coriandrum sativum*) seed

While bathing in vinegar may not sound like the most soothing activity, we think you'll love the feeling of this herb-infused vinegar on your sun-exposed skin!

## DIRECTIONS

Combine herbs in a half-gallon glass jar.

Pour apple cider vinegar over the herbs, ensuring that the vinegar is covering the herbs by at least 1 inch.

Place a square piece of natural waxed paper on top of the jar, then seal the jar with a lid (this protects the extract from any chemical coating that may be on the lid, and protects the lid from rusting when using vinegar).

Cap tightly, and give the jar a shake to ensure that the herbs and menstruum are thoroughly mixed.

Label the jar, store in a cool, dark location, and visit every 1–3 days, giving the jar a shake.

Let macerate for 4–6 weeks.

Line a wire strainer with a few layers of cheesecloth, or simply place the cheesecloth within a funnel placed in the mouth of a jar, and decant the mixture.

Strain the mixture through the cheesecloth and with clean, dry hands, gather the cloth up and squeeze strongly, squeezing as much liquid from the herbs as possible.

Transfer the liquid into a glass jar using a funnel.

Label, and store in a cool, dark place for up to 1 year.

To use this cooling bath, add 1–2 cups to bathwater.

# Antifungal
## FOOT BATH

### INGREDIENTS

1 gallon (128 fl oz) water

¼ cup chaparral
(*Larrea tridentata*) leaf

2 tbsp goldenseal
(*Hydrastis canadensis*) root,
sustainably sourced,
or Oregon grape
(*Berberis aquifolium*) root

2 tbsp thyme
(*Thymus vulgaris*)
aerial parts

2 tbsp sage
(*Salvia officinalis*)
aerial parts

2 cups (16 fl oz) raw apple
cider vinegar

½ cup Epsom salt

---

Heavy-hitting antifungal herbs
combine with apple cider
vinegar in a soak for fungal
foot infections.

### DIRECTIONS

Bring water to a boil in a large pot.
Turn off heat, add chaparral, goldenseal
or Oregon grape root, thyme, and sage,
and let infuse, covered, for 20 minutes.

Strain herbal infusion using a
wire mesh strainer.

In a foot basin or container large
enough for two feet, combine herbal
infusion, vinegar, and Epsom salt,
stirring thoroughly.

Soak feet in the warm foot bath
for at least 15 minutes.

Repeat as needed.

# *Too-Much-Sun*
# TEA BATH

This recipe is two-for-one: you'll make a lovely cooling iced tea and a soothing herbal bath at the same time! If you don't have access to a bathtub, use as a cool compress instead.

## INGREDIENTS

3 tbsp green tea (*Camellia sinensis*) leaf

2 tbsp tulsi (*Ocimum tenuiflorum*) aerial parts

1 tsp rose (*Rosa* spp.) petal or peppermint (*Mentha* x *piperita*) leaf

Ice

## DIRECTIONS

Combine all herbs in a quart-size glass jar and mix. Remove 2 heaping teaspoons of the herb blend and place into a smaller glass jar or teapot.

Add about 1 quart boiling water to the large jar (to make your bath tea) and 1 cup boiling water to the smaller jar or teapot (for your iced tea). Cover both.

Allow your tea to steep for 4 minutes, then strain only the small jar or teapot; leave the bath tea to continue steeping.

Fill a sturdy glass jar or drinking glass with ice, and slowly pour the warm tea over the ice—this will cool and dilute the tea to drinking strength.

Relax in the shade for another 15 minutes or so and enjoy your cooling iced tea while your bath tea steeps.

When you're ready, prepare a comfortably cool bath. Strain out the herbs and add your bath tea to the tub. Soak until you feel cool and refreshed!

# Bliss Bath
## FOR SORE MUSCLES

After a long day in the garden (or at the gym), try a hot soak with this ultra-relaxing bath blend. Lobelia is amazingly effective at helping to release muscular tension and spasm, but it's quite a potent herb; this is one herbal bath tea that does NOT double as a beverage!

* * *

### INGREDIENTS

⅛ cup lobelia (*Lobelia inflata*) aerial parts

2 tbsp fresh ginger (*Zingiber officinale*) rhizome, finely chopped or shredded

2 tbsp lavender (*Lavandula* spp.) flower bud

1 quart (32 fl oz) water

### DIRECTIONS

Bring the water to a boil in a small pot. Add the lobelia and ginger; reduce heat and simmer, covered, 10-15 minutes.

Turn off the heat and add the lavender flower buds; steep, covered, for another 10-15 minutes.

Strain out herbs and discard; add the liquid to a hot bath. Soak for as long as desired.

(This bath is not recommended for children.)

# Soothing
## YARROW AND HELICHRYSUM BATH

Yarrow is a versatile herb for protection from and recovery from the elements, windburn, sunburn, mosquito bites, and other outdoor itches, and is generally refreshing and health-promoting. This is very simple, but take care not to let any yarrow into the drain as it is stiff and tenacious.

### INGREDIENTS

1-2 cups fresh or dried yarrow (*Achillea millefolium*) aerial parts, chopped

1 tbsp (0.5 fl oz) sweet almond, grapeseed, or olive oil

5 drops helichrysum (*Helichrysum italiccum*) essential oil

### DIRECTIONS

Simmer the yarrow in a pot with 1 quart water for 10 minutes.

Remove from heat.

Strain thoroughly.

Combine carrier oil and essential oil in a small bowl and mix thoroughly.

Add the oil to the strained yarrow infusion.

Pour the liquid portion into bath. Take care to wipe down tub after bathing as the oil can create a slippery situation!

# BABY BATH: CALMING

Sometimes, nothing calms a baby (and maybe baby's caregivers, too!) like a warm, relaxing bath. Introduce your wee ones to herbs early in their life with this baby-safe bath blend, perfect for just before bed or during cranky time.

## INGREDIENTS

¼ cup chamomile (*Matricaria chamomilla*) flower

¼ cup lemon balm (*Melissa officinalis*) aerial parts

⅛ cup lavender (*Lavandula* spp.) flower bud

## DIRECTIONS

Add herbs to a heat-safe glass quart jar and pour just-off-the-boil water over them to fill the jar. Cover and let steep for 5–10 minutes.

Strain, and add to baby bath—adjust temperature as needed before adding the baby. This bath can also be used as a sponge bath.

# BABY BATH: FEVER EASE

A lukewarm bath can be helpful to bring down a baby's temperature, and the addition of catnip and elder not only add a diaphoretic component, but can also help to relax baby. If a warm bath is not an option for your little one, simply soak a washcloth in the bath "tea," and apply to baby's forehead.

## INGREDIENTS

¼ cup catnip (*Nepeta cataria*) aerial parts

¼ cup elder (*Sambucus canadensis* or *S. nigra*) flower

## DIRECTIONS

Add herbs to a heat-safe glass quart jar and pour just-off-the-boil water over them to fill the jar.

Cover and let steep for 5–10 minutes.

Strain, and add to baby bath—adjust temperature as needed (approximately 90–95 degrees F water is best for bringing down a fever) before adding the baby.

This bath can also be used as a sponge bath.

# POSTPARTUM
## Sitz Bath

### INGREDIENTS

1 cup calendula (*Calendula officinalis*) flower

½ cup lady's mantle (*Alchemilla vulgaris*) aerial parts

½ cup lavender (*Lavandula* spp.) flower bud

½ cup rose (*Rosa* spp.) petal

½ cup yarrow (*Achillea millefolium*) aerial parts

¼ cup myrrh (*Commiphora myrrha*) resin powder

½ cup sea salt

### DIRECTIONS

Combine herbal ingredients in a heat-safe glass half-gallon jar.

Pour just-off-the-boil water over the herbs, filling the jar to the top.

Cover and steep until warm but not too hot to touch (approximately 10 minutes).

Strain herbs through a fine mesh filter and pour "tea" and sea salt into a sitz bath.

Sit for 20-40 minutes daily during the first couple of weeks postpartum.

The vulnerary, astringent, and antimicrobial herbs in this postpartum sitz bath help to soothe perineal tissue, support the healing of vaginal and perineal tears, and ward off infection. Many of these herbs also have a calming aroma—perfect for the days and weeks after childbirth. For those that do not have access to a sitz bath, follow the same recipe, but use only 1 quart of hot water for a stronger brew that can then be diluted in a bathtub.

# Fl🌼wer
## FACIAL STEAM

A facial steam is a simple and decadent way to soften and cleanse skin and deliver the benefits of herbs. You can tailor the herbs to your skin type or the skin imbalance you are experiencing. Lavender, chamomile, and rose for dry/sensitive skin; yarrow, rose, and sage for oily skin; or pine needles, thyme, and green tea for acne-prone skin, for example. These aromatic herbs are also lovely nervines, so this doubles as a calming, meditative practice as well!

---

### INGREDIENTS

1 gallon (128 fl oz) water

2 tbsp lavender (*Lavandula* spp.) flower bud

2 tbsp chamomile (*Matricaria chamomilla*) flower

2 tbsp rose (*Rosa* spp.) petal

### DIRECTIONS

Bring water to a boil in a large pot or tea kettle.

Place a large, wide bowl on a table with a comfortable seat.

Add herbs to bowl, and then cover with the hot water.

Settle into the chair, then lean your face over the bowl at a comfortable distance so as not to burn your skin.

Drape a towel over your head to form a tent over the bowl, capturing the steam.

Enjoy the steam for 5–15 minutes.

❝

*Full-body soaking is a luxury to the senses*
*and no tub should be left unfilled.*

BOTANICAL SKIN CARE COURSE

57

# CHAPTER THREE

# BLEMISH PREPARATIONS

# BLEMISH PREPARATIONS

No matter how much care you give your skin,
breakouts happen. These simple recipes will
help tone down inflammation and irritation and
promote skin healing for speedy spot removal.

# Tamanu
# *Blemish Stick*

### INGREDIENTS
½ tbsp (0.25 fl oz) tamanu oil

½ tbsp (0.25 fl oz) rosehip seed oil

2 drops tea tree (*Melaleuca alternifolia*) essential oil

1 drop neroli (*Citrus x aurantium*) essential oil

### DIRECTIONS
Combine all ingredients in a ½-ounce roll-on dispenser and shake well. Don't forget to label!

Apply as needed to acne and blemish spots. Shake before each use. Not recommended for all-over use.

Store in a cool, dry place for up to 1 year.

You might be surprised to see an oil-based blemish balm. Tamanu and rosehip seed oils are low on the comedogenic scale and are strongly anti-inflammatory and soothing to the skin, while tea tree oil adds an astringent, antimicrobial finish.

# Herbal
## Spot Soother

Choose your favorite ingredients in this freeform recipe for a blemish spot mask. Choose from soothing and antimicrobial honey, moisturizing aloe gel, astringent apple cider vinegar, absorbent and anti-inflammatory French green clay, antimicrobial essential oils, and non-comedogenic jojoba oil.

### INGREDIENTS

Liquid (choose one):

Raw honey

Aloe (*Aloe vera*) leaf gel

Apple cider vinegar

French green clay

Tea tree (*Melaleuca alternifolia*),
lavender (*Lavandula* spp.), or
neem (*Azadirachta indica*) essential oil

Jojoba oil

### DIRECTIONS

Combine 1 teaspoon liquid with enough clay to make a paste. Add 1–2 drops essential oil diluted in ¼ teaspoon jojoba oil.

Dab onto blemish. Let dry and then gently rinse off with warm water. Gently pat skin dry with a clean towel.

CHAPTER FOUR

# CLEANSERS

# CLEANSERS

The simple act of washing your face is the first
step in maintaining healthy, balanced skin.
Many commercial soaps and cleansers can strip
away protective oils and alter skin pH, leaving it
prone to irritation and breakouts. These easy-to-
make cleansers include nourishing plant oils
and other ingredients to help keep your skin
in the sweet spot.

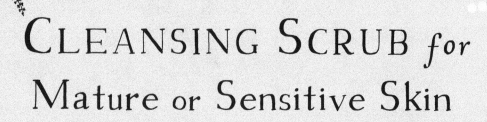

# CLEANSING SCRUB *for*
# Mature or Sensitive Skin

Emollient and protective herbs combine with the
cleansing power of oat or barley flour and a nourishing fat
in this scrub that cleanses and exfoliates mature
or sensitive facial skin.

### INGREDIENTS

1 tbsp oat or barley flour

1 tsp licorice (*Glycyrrhiza glabra*) root powder

1 tsp tulsi (*Ocimum tenuiflorum*) aerial parts powder

1 tbsp (0.5 fl oz) cream, milk of choice,
or argan oil

### DIRECTIONS

Mix dry ingredients together in a small bowl.

Slowly add cream, milk, or oil and stir to combine until
a thin paste forms.

Apply to face in circular movements, avoiding the eyes.

Rinse off with warm water. Gently pat skin dry
with a clean towel.

# CLEANSING SCRUB *for dry skin*

Mucilaginous herbs combine with the cleansing power of oat or almond and a nourishing fat in this scrub that cleanses and exfoliates dry facial skin.

## INGREDIENTS

1 tbsp oat or almond flour

1 tsp fenugreek (*Trigonella foenum-graecum*) seed powder

1 tsp comfrey (*Symphytum officinale*) leaf or root powder

1 tbsp (0.5 fl oz) cream, milk of choice, or sesame oil

## DIRECTIONS

Mix dry ingredients together in a small bowl.

Slowly add cream, milk, or oil and stir to combine until a thin paste forms.

Apply to face in circular movements, avoiding the eyes.

Rinse off with warm water. Gently pat skin dry with a clean towel.

# CLEANSING SCRUB *for oily skin*

Astringent herbs combine with the cleansing power of rice or chickpea flour in this scrub that cleanses and exfoliates oily facial skin.

## INGREDIENTS

1 tbsp rice or chickpea flour

1 tsp coriander (*Coriandrum sativum*) seed powder

1 tsp rose (*Rosa* spp.) petal powder

1 tbsp (0.5 fl oz) aloe (*Aloe vera*) leaf juice or rose (*Rosa* spp.) hydrosol

## DIRECTIONS

Mix dry ingredients together in a small bowl.

Slowly add aloe juice or rose hydrosol and stir to combine until a thin paste forms.

Apply to face in circular movements, avoiding the eyes.

Rinse off with warm water. Gently pat skin dry with a clean towel.

# *Foaming*
# HONEY CLEANSER

*Adapted from* Hello Glow: 150+ Easy Natural Beauty Recipes for a
Fresh New You *by Stephanie Gerber (Gerber. 2006).*

This daily cleanser balances out soap's drying nature by adding
honey as a humectant. For extra bubbly goodness,
use a foaming pump-top dispenser.

## INGREDIENTS

⅓ cup (2.7 fl oz) castile soap

⅓ cup (2.7 fl oz) raw honey

3 tbsp (1.5 fl oz) distilled water or hydrosol of your choice

1 tsp avocado or olive oil

5-7 drops essential oil of your choice (optional)

## DIRECTIONS

Combine the soap, honey, and water or hydrosol in a large
glass measuring cup. Mix gently to combine—try not to agitate
too much or you'll create a lot of foam!

Stir in the oil and if using, the essential oil.

Transfer to storage bottle with pump-top dispenser.
Label, and store in a cool, dark place for up to 3 months.

Apply to face in circular movements, avoiding the eyes.
Use daily as needed. If oils separate, swirl the bottle
gently to recombine.

# D.I.Y.

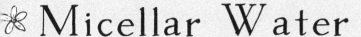

# Micellar Water

Micellar water contains tiny particles of oil suspended in water. It can be used as an all-in-one makeup remover, gentle cleanser, and toner. As always, customize this recipe to suit your needs by varying the hydrosol or using an infused oil.

## INGREDIENTS

1 cup (8 fl oz) rose (*Rosa* spp.), neroli (*Citrus* x *aurantium*), or other hydrosol of your choice

⅛ tsp lecithin, granular or liquid

½ tsp vegetable glycerin

½ tsp jojoba or argan oil

½ tsp castile soap

Natural preservative (optional)

## DIRECTIONS

Pour the hydrosol into a large glass measuring cup or jar, and place the measuring cup into a shallow pan of water.

Heat gently until the hydrosol is just about body temperature—check by spooning out a few drops onto your wrist: the hydrosol should feel neither hot nor cold on your skin. Remove the measuring cup from the hot water bath.

Add all other ingredients to the hydrosol, and mix thoroughly. (If you are using a preservative, be sure to follow the manufacturer's directions.)

Once any foam has dispersed and the mixture has cooled to room temperature, pour into a flip-top or squirt-top storage bottle and label. (Spray bottles won't work well for this.)

To use, moisten a cotton pad and gently wipe over the skin of the face, avoiding the eyes. No need to rinse!

Label, and store at room temperature for up to 3 months, or longer if refrigerated. If using preservative, shelf life will be longer.

# *Citrus Coconut*
# BODY WASH

*Adapted from 100 Organic Skin Care Recipes by Jessica Ress (Ress. 2014).*

This creamy body wash moisturizes as it cleanses, and the trio of citrus oils adds a zesty twist!

## INGREDIENTS

2-3 tbsp lemongrass (*Cymbopogon* spp.) stalk

½ cup (4 fl oz) coconut oil

½ cup (4 fl oz) raw honey

40 drops grapefruit (*Citrus x paradisi*) essential oil

25 drops lemon (*Citrus x limon*) essential oil

25 drops sweet orange (*Citrus x sinensis*) essential oil

1 cup (8 fl oz) unscented liquid castile soap

## DIRECTIONS

Prepare lemongrass-infused coconut oil using the instructions in the herb-infused oil tutorial.

While it's still warm and liquid, transfer the infused coconut oil to a bowl and stir in honey.

Add the essential oils and stir well to combine.

Pour in the castile soap and stir very gently to combine; vigorous stirring or whisking will cause the soap to foam.

Use a funnel to transfer the body wash to a 16-ounce squeeze top bottle. Label, and store in a cool, dark place for up to 1 year.

Shake well before each use.

# Toning Witch Hazel
## CLEANSER

Adapted from Natural Beauty Alchemy by Fifi M. Maacaron
(Maacaron. 2015).

### INGREDIENTS

1 tsp vegetable glycerin

2 tbsp (1 fl oz) witch hazel (*Hamamelis virginiana*) bark extract

2 tbsp (1 fl oz) aloe (*Aloe vera*) leaf gel

2 tbsp (1 fl oz) castile soap

15 drops tea tree (*Melaleuca alternifolia*) essential oil (optional)

### DIRECTIONS

In a glass measuring cup, combine glycerin, witch hazel extract,
and aloe gel, stirring well.

Place castile soap and essential oil (if using) in a bowl, stirring gently to
combine. Slowly add the glycerin/witch hazel/aloe gel in a thin stream,
whisking constantly, but gently as to avoid excess foaming.

Let mixture rest once combined.

Transfer to a pump bottle and label.

Prior to use, shake pump bottle. Wet face, then apply a small amount
of cleanser. Rub into skin gently to create a foaming action.

Rinse with warm water. Gently pat skin dry with a clean towel.

Follow with moisturizer.

Store cleanser in a cool, dark place for up to 6 months.

This gentle, foaming cleanser is perfect for acne-prone skin
(leave out the essential oil for an all-purpose skin cleanser).

# Almond and Rose
## CLEANSING CREAM

*Adapted from* Forgotten Ways for Modern Days *by* Rachel Blondel *(Blondel. 2016).*

This cleansing cream gently scrubs to remove dirt and makeup while it moisturizes the skin. This makes a small batch, so feel free to double it if you'd like to have enough to share.

## INGREDIENTS

¼ cup (2 fl oz) sweet almond oil

1 tbsp beeswax

¼ tsp vitamin E oil

¼ cup (2 fl oz) rose (*Rosa* spp.) hydrosol

1 tbsp almond flour

Natural preservative (optional)

## DIRECTIONS

Gently heat sweet almond oil and beeswax in a double boiler (or glass bowl over a saucepan of simmering water) until melted. Stir until mixture is melted and consistent. Remove from heat and transfer to a blender or a bowl (if using immersion blender) to cool.

If using a natural preservative that needs to be added to the water phase, add to the hydrosol now and stir well; otherwise, wait until after cream has emulsified.

Once oil mixture has cooled to room temperature and looks creamy and semi-solid, add vitamin E oil.

Turning blender on low-medium setting or using an immersion blender in a bowl, slowly add hydrosol mixture to oil mixture while blending. Mixture will begin to emulsify and become creamy. Avoid overmixing. Cream will set up a bit more as it cools.

Stir in almond flour.

Pour cream into sterilized glass jars, label, and store in the refrigerator for 1-2 weeks (if using a preservative, shelf life will be longer).

To use, transfer or squeeze a bit of cleansing cream onto fingers, rub into facial skin, and then gently remove with a tissue or cotton pad.

*Using herbs in everyday life, including do-it-yourself bath products, is an opportunity to steep your entire being in the magic of plants and deepens your understanding of individual herbs and their actions.*

BOTANICAL SKIN CARE COURSE

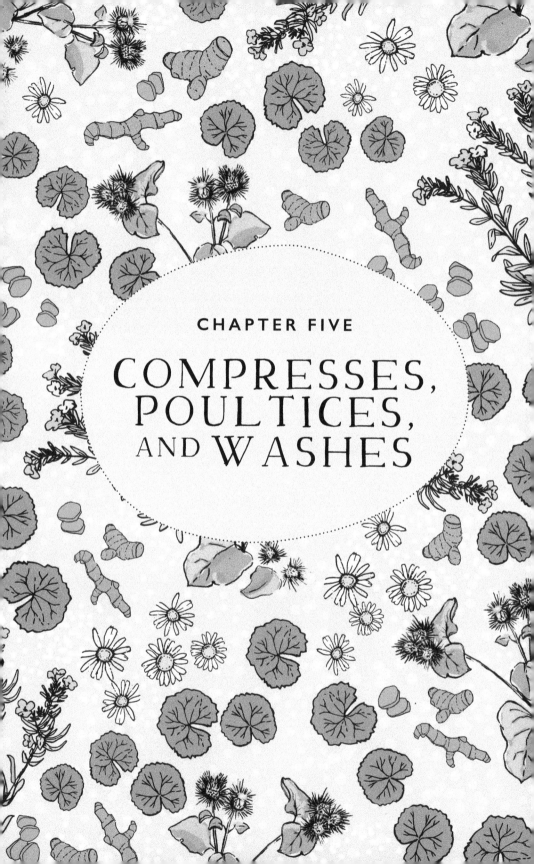

CHAPTER FIVE

# COMPRESSES, POULTICES, AND WASHES

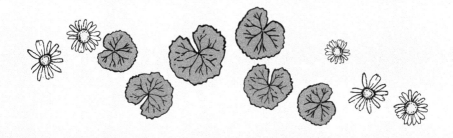

# COMPRESSES, POULTICES, AND WASHES

These topical preparations are among the simplest ways to use herbs in basic first aid and skin care—they don't require any advance preparation, and herbs and water are all you need. Poultices, compresses, and washes can help speed healing of wounds, bruises, bites, stings, burns, and soft tissue injuries. They also help promote circulation, ease pain and inflammation, and can help resolve skin conditions such as eczema and acne.

Virtually any skin-soothing, vulnerary herb can be used in a poultice, compress, or wash. These recipes highlight a few wonderful combinations and will give you a sense of the wide variety of ways you can use these versatile preparations.

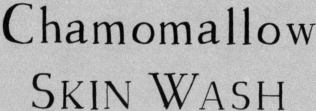

# Chamomallow
# Skin Wash

Use as a topical wash or compress for itchy, inflamed skin.

### INGREDIENTS

½ cup chamomile (*Matricaria chamomilla*) flower

½ cup marshmallow (*Althaea officinalis*) root

1 quart (32 fl oz) water

### DIRECTIONS

Bring water to boil.

Add chamomile to a 1-quart jar and pour water over herb.

Let steep for 20-30 minutes.

Once chamomile has cooled a bit, add marshmallow root
& let steep for another 30 minutes (the mucilage in
marshmallow is extracted best in cooler water).

Strain the herbs from the infusion using a wire strainer
lined with a couple of layers of cheesecloth.

Use as a wash by pouring infusion directly onto itchy skin
or adding to the bathtub.

Alternatively, use as a compress by dipping a clean cloth in the
infusion and squeezing out excess liquid.

Apply to itchy skin and feel the soothing sensation!

Dip cloth again, squeeze out excess, and reapply as needed.

# *Herbal Vinegar*
## SKIN WASH

This recipe combines cooling vulnerary and anti-inflammatory herbs that can be used as a spray, compress, or all-over soak. This makes a big batch, so feel free to halve or even quarter the batch based on your needs.

### INGREDIENTS

3 cups (24 fl oz) raw apple cider vinegar

2 cups (16 fl oz) helichrysum (*Helichrysum italicum*), lavender (*Lavandula* spp.), or yarrow (*Achillea millefolium*) hydrosol

⅓ cup calendula (*Calendula officinalis*) flower

⅓ cup plantain (*Plantago* spp.) leaf

¼ cup chamomile (*Matricaria chamomilla*) flower

¼ cup Oregon grape (*Berberis aquifolium*) root

### DIRECTIONS

Place herbs in a quart glass jar and cover with vinegar so that it rises 1-2 inches above the herbs.

Cover tightly, placing a piece of natural waxed paper between the lid and the jar to protect the lid from corrosion by the vinegar and let sit for 2-3 weeks. Shake every few days, and add a splash of vinegar if needed to keep the vinegar level above the herbs once they absorb liquid and expand.

Strain herbs from vinegar and reserve the liquid. Compost the herbs.

Add hydrosol of choice to herbal vinegar.

Rebottle, label, and store in a cool, dark place for 6-12 months.

To use, gently dab across skin with a soft cloth or cotton ball or add a cup to bathwater!

# Gotu Kola & Oat
# CLAY PACK

## INGREDIENTS

2 tbsp oat flour

1 tbsp gotu kola (*Centella asiatica*) leaf powder

1 tbsp kaolin (white cosmetic) clay

2 tbsp (1 fl oz) water

½ tbsp (0.25 fl oz) jojoba or grapeseed oil

2 drops Roman chamomile (*Chamaemelum nobile*)
essential oil (optional)

## DIRECTIONS

Mix dry ingredients together thoroughly in a bowl or glass jar.

Add water and stir to combine.

Combine essential oil and jojoba or grapeseed oil in a small
container, then add to the other ingredients
and stir until combined.

Apply a thin layer to itchy skin; allow it to dry,
then rinse off with warm water.

Alternately, apply a warm, damp cloth over the clay pack, cover
with flannel for warmth, and keep on the skin for an extended
period as a poultice before rinsing off.

Store any extra clay pack in the refrigerator
and use within 2 days.

This makes a generous batch, so halve the recipe
if you want to use on small patches of itchy skin.

# LEMON AND SPEARMINT
# Elbow Lightener

*Adapted from* Jeanne Rose's Kitchen Cosmetics *by* Jeanne Rose *(Rose. 1990).*

If dead skin cells build up on the surface of the skin, it can become itchy, raised, flaky, and/or discolored. In this recipe, lemon juice lightens and astringent spearmint soothes; together, they encourage exfoliation and renewal. The name suggests use on elbows, but this preparation can be applied to other areas of the skin, as long as they are not especially sensitive.

## INGREDIENTS

½–¾ cup fresh spearmint (*Mentha spicata*) leaf, chopped

½ lemon, juiced

## DIRECTIONS

Decoct spearmint in ¾–1 cup water until it is reduced to about ½ cup.

Strain out the spearmint and add the lemon juice.

Mix, and allow to cool. Refrigerate to store up to 48 hours.

To use, apply the liquid with cotton pads to the elbows or other desired area.

Allow to dry, then repeat application.

Reapply 3–4 times to each area.

# Anti-Itch Paste

*Adapted from* 100 Organic Skincare Recipes *by* Jessica Ress *(Ress. 2014).*

Taking care of the itchy-scratchies is as easy as combining vinegar and baking soda!

## INGREDIENTS

1 tsp apple cider vinegar

1 tbsp baking soda

## DIRECTIONS

Combine ingredients in a bowl or jar and mix to form a thick paste. It will bubble up at first, but will eventually settle as it is stirred.

Apply as needed to bites, stings, and sunburn.

Store in a closed container in the refrigerator for up to 2 weeks; stir before using.

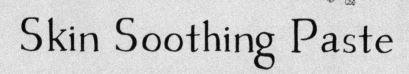

# Skin Soothing Paste

*Adapted from Brenda Igler (Igler. 2016).*

One of the chief ingredients in this skin paste is neem (*Azadirachta indica*) leaf. Neem has many applications for balancing skin issues, and may be used both internally and externally to that end.

## INGREDIENTS

2 parts neem (*Azadirachta indica*) leaf powder

2 parts echinacea (*Echinacea* spp.) leaf powder

2 parts comfrey (*Symphytum officinale*) leaf powder

1 part yellow dock (*Rumex crispus*) root powder

1 part burdock (*Arctium lappa*) root powder

1 part turmeric (*Curcuma longa*) rhizome powder

Aloe (*Aloe vera*) leaf gel or sesame oil (adjust amount as needed to achieve desired consistency.)

## DIRECTIONS

Define your "part" based on how big of a batch you want to make—for a small batch, 1 part could equal 1 teaspoon: for a larger batch, 1 part could equal 1 tablespoon or ¼ cup.

Combine all ingredients in a bowl and stir until thoroughly mixed.

Mix 1 teaspoon of powder with either aloe (*Aloe vera*) leaf gel or sesame oil. (Sesame oil is preferred if there is significant dryness in the skin.)

Apply to affected area and cover with a bandage.

This paste can remain on the skin for several hours.

# Cold Sore
# COMPRESS

*Adapted from* Herbal Body Book *by Jeanne Rose (Rose, 2000).*

This is a simple, oil-free herbal recipe designed for cold sores, with the interesting base of applesauce (unsweetened is highly suggested for this use!) or apple for additional soothing. Note that this apple-based product may brown in a few days, or after frozen, but that is normal.

## INGREDIENTS

1 tbsp borage (*Borago officinalis*) flower (fresh if possible)

2 tbsp white willow (*Salix alba*) bark

1 tbsp celandine (*Chelidonium majus*) aerial parts

1 tbsp marshmallow (*Althaea officinalis*) root

1 tbsp comfrey (*Symphytum officinalis*) root

½ cup applesauce or 1 small, sliced apple

## DIRECTIONS

Combine dry ingredients.

When ready to use, place herbs in a small pot.

Add ½ cup applesauce or 1 small, sliced apple to the pot, along with fresh borage flowers (if using).

Pour 1–1½ cups of boiling water over this mixture, enough to more than cover herbs.

Bring to a boil, then simmer for 5 minutes.

Allow to cool.

Strain through a cheesecloth-lined strainer.

Use the cooled, strained mixture as a compress on cold sores for 10 minutes twice daily while affected.

This fresh preparation should last 1–3 days in the refrigerator.

Alternatively, portions can be frozen and thawed for use for 1–2 weeks.

# Liniment or Poultice for
# KELOID-PRONE SKIN

*Adapted from* Herbal Formularies for Health Professionals Vol. 1 by
*Jill Stansbury (Stansbury. 2018).*

The sulfur content of garlic (and other *Allium* species) helps
promote healthy connective tissue regeneration; combined with
anti-inflammatory turmeric and scar-softening gotu kola, this
recipe may help to keep keloids at bay when applied to wounds
with scar potential.

## INGREDIENTS

1 tsp turmeric (*Curcuma longa*) rhizome tincture or powder

1 tsp garlic (*Allium sativum*) bulb tincture or powder

1 tsp gotu kola (*Centella asiatica*) leaf tincture or powder

## DIRECTIONS

If using tinctures, soak a cotton ball or gauze pad in the
combined tinctures and tape to wound.

If using powders, mix the combined powders with a small
amount of water to form a thin paste. Spread paste between
two pieces of muslin and apply to wound.

# TURMERIC HONEY

While honey alone makes an excellent support for burns, the addition of turmeric, which has been used for centuries in ayurvedic medicine to ease burns and other skin inflammation (Lad, 1998), makes it extra soothing. Make a large batch for the first aid kit by following the recipe below, or simply combine 1 tablespoon of honey with ¼ teaspoon of turmeric as needed.

## INGREDIENTS

⅛ cup turmeric (*Curcuma longa*) rhizome powder

1½ cups (12 fl oz) raw honey

## DIRECTIONS

Place turmeric powder in a clean, dry glass jar and cover with honey.

Stir with a clean, dry spoon, and cover jar with a tightly sealed lid.

Label, and store in a cool, dark place for up to 1 year.

Apply topically to burns, or mix in hot water for a sweetened turmeric tea!

# WOUND WASH

Yarrow is the ultimate wound herb with its antimicrobial, styptic, and vulnerary properties. Combined with resinous and vulnerary calendula and antimicrobial barberry, this threesome packs a powerful punch for warding off infection and supporting the healing process of minor wounds.

## INGREDIENTS

1 tbsp (0.5 fl oz) yarrow (*Achillea millefolium*) aerial parts tincture

1½ tsp calendula (*Calendula officinalis*) flower tincture

1½ tsp barberry (*Berberis* spp.) root tincture

## DIRECTIONS

Combine tinctures in a 1-ounce glass dropper bottle.

Shake well.

Label, and store in a cool, dark place.

To use, pour 1–2 droppersful on minor wounds.

CHAPTER SIX

# COSMETICS

# COSMETICS

Just like other skin, hair, and beauty products,
commercial cosmetics such as lipstick, mascara,
and eyeshadow can contain problematic ingredients
you may prefer to avoid. Fortunately for those who
love to freshen the face with a touch of decoration,
you can make simple cosmetic preparations
at home!

# Herbal Eyeshadow
## POWDER

Herbal eyeshadow is a bit of a different experience than commercial mineral eyeshadows, so experimentation is needed to find what works best for you. We have provided two eyeshadow options below—you can either make a powder eyeshadow with herbs and clays and use as-is, or add shea butter to increase its adhering ability. Note that it can be helpful to have a slightly moisturized eyelid before applying (especially if you choose to leave out the shea butter!). It is also best to use very finely ground powders, so purchasing your ingredients pre-powdered is preferable. Clay is a silky carrier that can also add color, so it's often helpful to add a bit of clay to each blend.

## INGREDIENTS
### 1–2 TSP OF ONE OR MORE OF THE FOLLOWING:

Activated charcoal powder (BLACK/GRAY)

Cocoa powder (BROWN)

Sassafras (*Sassafras* spp.) bark powder (BROWN)

Schisandra (*Schisandra chinensis*) berry powder (RED-BROWN)

Cinnamon (*Cinnamomum* spp.) bark powder (RED-BROWN)

Alkanet (*Alkanna tinctoria*) root powder (RED)

Paprika (*Capsicum annuum*) fruit powder (RED)

Beet (*Beta vulgaris*) root powder (PINK)

Turmeric (*Curcuma longa*) rhizome powder (GOLDEN)

Calendula (*Calendula officinalis*) flower powder (YELLOW)

Spirulina (*Spirulina* spp.) powder (GREEN)

Nettle (*Urtica dioica*) leaf powder (LIGHT GREEN)

Marshmallow (*Althaea officinalis*) root powder (WHITE)

Clays of choice

Mica powders of choice

¼–1 tsp shea butter (optional)

2–5 drops of oil of choice (e.g., jojoba oil, grapeseed oil, sweet almond oil) (optional)

84

## DIRECTIONS

Combine small amounts of one or more of the herbal powders until you reach your desired shade. Add more clay or arrowroot powder to lighten the shade.

If adding shea butter, place powdered mixture into the bowl of a mortar and pestle, add shea butter, and grind together until shea is well-incorporated. Note that only a small amount of shea butter is needed—if you add too much shea butter, the mixture will get clumpy and you will need to add additional powder. The eyeshadow should still look like powder once the shea is added.

Transfer to a clean, dry container, and label. Store in a cool, dark place for up to 1 year. To apply eyeshadow, first apply a bit of lotion or cream moisturizer to eyelids. Once this has mostly absorbed into the skin, apply the eyeshadow, using a small brush.

If you find that the eyeshadow is not sticking, or if it feels too rough on the skin, add a few drops of oil or serum to the mixture, mix well, and reapply.

## SOME SAMPLE FORMULAS:

### RED-BROWN:

½ tsp alkanet powder + ½ tsp cocoa powder + a sprinkle of gold mica

### PINK:

1 tsp beetroot powder + ¼ tsp kaolin clay + a sprinkle of gold mica

### YELLOW-BROWN:

1 tsp cocoa + ½ tsp turmeric + a generous sprinkle of gold mica

# BLUSH STICK

A simple recipe that adds rosy color to cheeks! Can be used as a lip gloss, too.

## INGREDIENTS

¼ cup shea butter

1 tsp alkanet (*Alkanna tinctoria*) root powder

## DIRECTIONS

Heat the shea butter in a double boiler over low heat (or a glass or ceramic bowl or heat-safe glass jar over a small saucepan of simmering water) until melted.

Take off the heat and mix in alkanet powder until combined.

Pour into lip balm tubes or small deodorant tubes.

Allow to cool before covering.

To apply, sweep along cheekbones and then use finger or sponge to blend into skin.

# NATURAL MASCARA
## AND EYELINER

*Adapted from Katie Wells (Wells. 2019e).*

This recipe is for black mascara or eyeliner, but you can substitute cocoa powder for the activated charcoal for a brown shade.

## INGREDIENTS

2 capsules activated charcoal

½ tsp bentonite clay

¼ tsp vegetable glycerin

½ tsp aloe (*Aloe vera*) leaf gel

## DIRECTIONS

Combine activated charcoal and clay in a very small bowl, mixing well to achieve a consistent color.

Add glycerin and aloe gel. Stir well until mixture is smooth.

Transfer to mascara container using a tincture bottle dropper or even a plastic bag with the tiniest bit of the corner cut off
(like when piping frosting).

# NATURAL
# LIQUID FOUNDATION

*Adapted from Katie Wells (Wells. 2019d).*

## INGREDIENTS

2 tsp zinc oxide or 1 tsp zinc oxide and 1 tsp arrowroot powder

A sprinkle to ⅛ tsp gold mica dust

1 tsp rhassoul powder (other clays can be selected to suit your skin tone)

2-3 tsp finely ground cocoa powder (adjust to achieve desired color)

1 tsp translucent mica powder (optional, best for oily skin)

Favorite facial lotion

## DIRECTIONS

Combine all ingredients in a mixing bowl, starting with the
white or translucent ingredients first.

Add the pigmented ingredients slowly, whisking periodically
to check the color of the mixture.

Once you've reached the appropriate shade, swatch it on your inner arm.

Make sure ingredients are fully blended, and store in a glass jar
with a lid.

Mix your finished powder with a basic lotion. Simply add equal
parts lotion and powder mixture or tweak to obtain the consistency
you prefer.

---

This recipe can be adapted to give light to medium coverage. For
a lighter foundation, use less zinc oxide; omit the arrowroot and
add extra zinc oxide for more coverage and a matte finish. Mineral
ingredients like zinc oxide and mica powders can be purchased
online. Note that zinc oxide powder poses some potential health
risks if it's inhaled; be sure to use a dust mask when mixing the
ingredients in this recipe.

# *Alkanet*
# LIP BALM

## *INGREDIENTS*

1–2 tsp alkanet (*Alkanna tinctoria*) root powder

1 tbsp (0.5 fl oz) coconut oil

1 tbsp (0.5 fl oz) olive oil

1 ½ tsp shea butter

1 tbsp beeswax

⅛ tsp vitamin E oil

Up to 10 drops vanilla (*Vanilla planifolia*)
$CO_2$ extract, or coriander (*Coriandrum sativum*)
essential oil (optional)

## *DIRECTIONS*

Combine alkanet powder, coconut oil, olive oil, and shea butter in a double boiler over low heat (or a glass or ceramic bowl over a small saucepan of simmering water), stirring occasionally until completely melted. The red coloring of the root will begin to saturate the oil immediately. Use a cooking thermometer to monitor the temperature, keeping it below 120 degrees F.

Once butter has melted, keep the oil mixture warm to allow alkanet's pigments to saturate the oil. Simmer water in double boiler for approximately 30 minutes — keep an eye on the water level so that it doesn't evaporate completely.

Remove from heat and strain through several layers of fine cheesecloth or a natural coffee filter to separate the oil from the alkanet powder.

Return strained oil to double boiler and add beeswax, warming until melted.

Remove from heat and let cool a bit, then stir in vitamin E oil and essential oil (if using).

Pour into tins or tubes and allow to cool.

Once cool, label and date the tins. This preparation should keep for about 6 months in a cool, dry place (longer, if stored in the refrigerator).

This balm is moisturizing to the lips and a pretty red color, too! Adjust the amount of alkanet root powder based on the depth of color you would like to achieve.

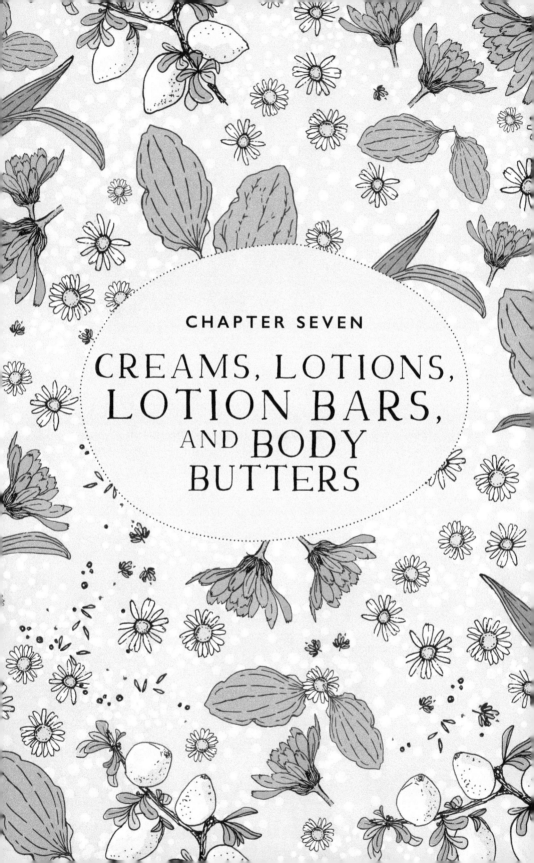

CHAPTER SEVEN

# CREAMS, LOTIONS, LOTION BARS, AND BODY BUTTERS

# CREAMS, LOTIONS, LOTION BARS, AND BODY BUTTERS

Keeping your skin hydrated and supple isn't just a question of appearance—maintaining skin moisture can soothe symptoms of imbalance, nourish the cells of the skin, and help restore the barrier integrity that's so important for overall skin function.

Creams, lotions, and body butters are fantastic options for keeping your skin soft and nourished—and they can all be made at home, using simple ingredients and some basic kitchen equipment!

# BASIC CREAM

*Adapted from Rosemary Gladstar and Bevin Clare (Gladstar & Clare. 2010).*

This recipe is for a basic cream. Oils can be infused with wellness-promoting herbs to achieve specific actions.

## INGREDIENTS

⅔ cup (5.3 fl oz) distilled water, hydrosol, or well-strained herbal tea

⅓ cup (2.7 fl oz) aloe (*Aloe vera*) leaf gel

¾ cup (6 fl oz) carrier oil (e.g., olive, grapeseed, sweet almond, avocado, apricot, herb-infused)

¼ cup (2 fl oz) coconut oil

1–3 tsp cocoa butter or shea butter, depending on desired thickness

1 tsp liquid lecithin

2–4 tbsp beeswax

1–10 drops essential oil(s) of choice

1 tsp vitamin E oil

Natural preservative (optional)

## DIRECTIONS

Combine distilled water and aloe gel in a glass measuring cup. Set aside. (Note: tap water can be used, but it may introduce bacteria and encourage mold growth.) If using a natural preservative that needs to be added to the water phase, add now and stir well; otherwise, wait until after cream has emulsified.

Combine carrier oil, coconut oil, butter, lecithin, and beeswax in a double boiler over low heat (or a glass or ceramic bowl or canning jar over a small saucepan of simmering water), stirring occasionally until completely melted.

Pour the oil and wax mixture into a large bowl and stir frequently until it cools to room temperature. The mixture should become thick, creamy, and semi-solid. The color should resemble that of vanilla pudding. This cooling process can be hastened in the refrigerator, but keep an eye on it so it doesn't get too hard.

When cooled, pour the oil mix into a blender.
Add the essential oil(s), if desired, and vitamin
E oil. Turn the blender on its highest speed.
In a slow, thin drizzle, pour the water and aloe
mixture into the center vortex.

When most of the water mixture has been
added to the oils, listen to the blender and
watch the cream. When the blender begins to
cough and choke, and the cream looks thick
and white like buttercream frosting, turn off
the blender. You can slowly add more water,
beating it in by hand with a spoon,
but don't over-beat!
The cream will thicken as it sets.

Pour the cream into sterilized jars, label,
and store in the refrigerator for 1-2 weeks
(if using a preservative, shelf life will
be longer).

# BASIC LOTION

*Adapted from Rosemary Gladstar and Bevin Clare (Gladstar & Clare. 2010).*

Making a lotion is similar to making a cream, and they have very similar ingredient lists. The main difference is that lotions contain more water than oil, compared to the even ratio of oil to water in creams. Lotions also contain a smaller amount of oils that are solid at room temperature, such as cocoa butter, shea butter, and coconut oil, which makes them a bit runnier than a cream. Lastly, when combining the water and oil components of a lotion, the oil ingredients are poured into the water, which is the opposite of how these ingredients are combined in a cream.

## INGREDIENTS

1 cup (8 fl oz) distilled water, hydrosol, or well-strained herbal tea (alternatively, ¼ cup of alcohol (95%) can be added to the water mixture as a preservative: if this route is chosen, use ¾ cup of distilled water so that the water/alcohol mixture equals 1 cup)

¾ cup (6 fl oz) carrier oil (e.g., olive, grapeseed, almond, avocado, apricot, herb-infused)

1 tbsp beeswax

1-10 drops essential oil(s) of choice

Natural preservative (optional)

## DIRECTIONS

Pour water ingredients into a blender. If using a natural preservative that needs to be added to the water phase, add now and stir well; otherwise, wait until after lotion has emulsified.

Combine oil and beeswax in a double boiler over low heat (or a glass or ceramic bowl or canning jar over a small saucepan of simmering water), stirring occasionally until completely melted.

Remove the oil/wax mixture from the heat, and set aside, letting it cool for a few minutes until the edges of the mixture begin to harden.

Turn the blender on high speed and slowly add the oil/wax mixture.

The emulsion should begin to harden after ⅔ of the oil/wax mixture has been added to the water. Continue adding the oil/wax mixture until it is all incorporated.

Toward the end of the emulsification process, the sides of the blender may occasionally need to be scraped. To do this, turn off the blender momentarily.

Once the lotion is silky and smooth, turn off the blender.

If desired, add essential oil(s) by folding them in with a spatula, or turning the blender on low, just long enough to incorporate the oils.

Pour the lotion into sterilized jars, label, and store in the refrigerator for 1–2 weeks (if using a preservative, shelf life will be longer).

# BASIC
# BODY BUTTER

*Adapted from Rosemary Gladstar and Bevin Clare (Gladstar & Clare. 2010).*

Body butter traditionally contains either mostly or only oil-based ingredients, which makes it a very thick skin preparation. Body butter can be used for skin that is chronically dry, cracked, and in need of protection. However, because of its high oil content, body butter may feel greasy for some skin types or if it isn't made properly.

Here is a simple recipe for a skin-nourishing body butter that includes vitamin E, an antioxidant that helps reduce scarring, fine lines, and wrinkles (Gladstar, 2008).

## INGREDIENTS

½ cup shea or cocoa butter

¼ cup (2 fl oz) coconut oil

¼ cup (2 fl oz) extra virgin olive oil

1 tsp vitamin E oil

20-30 drops of essential oil(s) (optional)

## DIRECTIONS

Gently heat cocoa butter in a double boiler over low heat (or a glass or ceramic bowl or canning jar over a small saucepan of simmering water) until melted. Add the oils, stir until mixture is melted and consistent, and turn off the heat.

Let cool for approximately 10 minutes, and once it is still warm, but not hot to the touch, cover and transfer to the refrigerator for approximately 1 hour, or until there is no longer a semi-liquid center.

Using an immersion blender or electric mixer, whip the mixture on high for 5 minutes, or until it changes color and looks fluffy. You may need to periodically scrape the mixture from the sides of the bowl.

Add vitamin E oil and essential oil (if desired), and mix.

Label, and store in a cool, dark place. This recipe will keep for up to 1 year.

Note: When storing body butter, it's important to remember that it may liquify when the weather is warm, which may make it difficult to use on the skin. If a batch of body butter has liquefied, just repeat steps 2 and 3. To prevent this from happening to a new batch of body butter, it's perfectly fine to store it in the refrigerator.

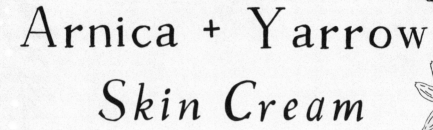

# Arnica + Yarrow Skin Cream

## INGREDIENTS

¼ cup (2 fl oz) arnica (*Arnica* spp.) flower-infused jojoba oil

2½ tbsp mango butter

1 tbsp beeswax

½ tsp vitamin E oil

¼ cup (2 fl oz) yarrow (*Achillea millefolium*) flower infusion
made with distilled water

2½ tbsp (1.25 fl oz) aloe (*Aloe vera*) leaf gel

Natural preservative (optional)

## DIRECTIONS

Make the arnica-infused oil using the instructions in the herb-
infused oil tutorial. Note that ¼ cup is the amount of finished herbal
oil to include in the recipe—you may need to start with more oil
when making the herb-infused oil, as the herbs will soak up some of
the oil (if you forget to do this, just top off with some plain oil as
needed for this recipe).

To prepare the yarrow infusion, combine 2 tablespoons yarrow
aerial parts and ½ cup just-off-the-boil distilled water, steep 20
minutes covered, and strain. Measure out ¼ cup and add aloe gel.
If using a natural preservative that needs to be added to the water
phase, add now and stir well; otherwise, wait until after
cream has emulsified.

Place infused oil, mango butter, and beeswax in a double boiler over low heat (or glass bowl over a saucepan of simmering water) until beeswax and mango butter have melted. Stir to blend. Remove from heat and transfer to a blender or a bowl (if using immersion blender) to cool.

Once oil mixture has cooled to room temperature and looks creamy and semi-solid, add vitamin E oil.

Turning blender on low-medium setting or using an immersion blender in a bowl, slowly add yarrow infusion mixture to oil mixture while blending. Mixture will begin to emulsify and become creamy. Avoid overmixing. Cream will set up a bit more as it cools.

Pour cream into sterilized glass jars, label, and store in the refrigerator for 1-2 weeks (if using a preservative, shelf life will be longer).

Arnica oil is a mainstay in many herbal first aid kits, as an anti-inflammatory, analgesic, vulnerary, and rubefacient used to support healing and ease pain, swelling, and bruising associated with fractures, sprains, and other injuries. Arnica combines well with yarrow in this soothing cream for aches, pains, bruises, and injuries.

# Rich Comfrey Root
# RESTORATION CREAM

*Adapted from* Herbal Body Book *by Jeanne Rose (Rose. 2000).*

## INGREDIENTS

¼ cup cocoa butter

½ cup (4 fl oz) avocado oil

¼ cup comfrey (*Symphytum officinale*) root, fresh or dried

2 cups (16 fl oz) water

Natural preservative (optional)

This recipe is quick to whip up— no herb-infused oil required!— and leaves the skin feeling well-nourished.

## DIRECTIONS

Simmer the comfrey root in 2 cups of water in a covered pot for 20 minutes.

Let this solution cool, then strain and save the liquid decoction. Measure out ¾ cup of comfrey decoction. You will use between ½–¾ cup decoction in this lotion.

If using a natural preservative that needs to be added to the water phase, add to the comfrey decoction now and stir well; otherwise, wait until after cream has emulsified.

Gently heat cocoa butter in a double boiler (or glass bowl over a saucepan of simmering water) until melted. Add the avocado oil, stir until mixture is melted and consistent, and turn off the heat.

Once oil mixture has cooled to room temperature and looks creamy and semi-solid, transfer to blender.

Turning blender on medium setting or using an immersion blender in a bowl, slowly add comfrey decoction to oil mixture while blending. Mixture will begin to emulsify and become creamy. ½ cup of comfrey decoction may be enough; if the cream has thickened, don't add more comfrey decoction. Avoid overmixing.

Pour cream into sterilized bottles or jars, label, and store in the refrigerator for 1–2 weeks (if using a preservative, shelf life will be longer).

# Gardener's
# HAND CREAM

This nourishing and richly moisturizing hand cream is perfect for dry, cracked hands that have been in the soil all day!

## INGREDIENTS

⅔ cup (5.3 fl oz) calendula (*Calendula officinalis*) hydrosol

⅓ cup (2.7 fl oz) aloe (*Aloe vera*) leaf gel

¾ cup (6 fl oz) baobab oil infused with comfrey (*Symphytum officinale*) root (sweet almond or avocado oil can be used instead of baobab oil)

5 tbsp mango butter

2 tbsp beeswax

1 tsp vitamin E oil

Natural preservative (optional)

## DIRECTIONS

Combine hydrosol and aloe gel in a glass measuring cup. If using a natural preservative that needs to be added to the water phase, add it now to hydrosol and stir well; otherwise, wait until after cream has emulsified. Set aside.

Gently heat oil, mango butter, and beeswax in a double boiler over low heat (or a glass or ceramic bowl or canning jar over a small saucepan of simmering water) until butter and beeswax are melted. Stir thoroughly to ensure ingredients are well-blended. Remove from heat and allow to cool.

Once oil mixture has come to room temperature and looks semi-solid, stir in vitamin E oil.

Transfer the oil mixture into a blender. Gradually add the hydrosol mixture to the oil and wax mixture in a thin stream until mixture becomes white and creamy. Avoid overmixing. Pour into sterilized jars or bottles and label. Store in the refrigerator for 1-2 weeks (if using a preservative, shelf life will be longer).

# DAILY MOISTURIZER
## *for* Acne-Prone Skin

### INGREDIENTS

⅓ cup (2.7 fl oz) saw palmetto (*Serenoa repens*)
berry-infused argan oil

2½ tbsp mango butter

2 tsp beeswax

½ tsp vitamin E oil

⅓ cup (2.7 fl oz) well-strained meadowsweet (*Filipendula ulmaria*) aerial parts infusion made with distilled water

2½ tbsp (1.25 fl oz) aloe (*Aloe vera*) leaf gel

45 drops tea tree (*Melaleuca alternifolia*) essential oil (optional)

Natural preservative (optional)

### DIRECTIONS

Make the saw palmetto berry-infused oil using the instructions in the herb-infused oil tutorial. Note that ⅓ cup is the amount of finished herbal oil to include in the recipe—you may need to start with more oil when making the herb-infused oil, as the herbs will soak up some of the oil (if you forget to do this, just top off with some plain oil as needed for this recipe).

To prepare the meadowsweet infusion, combine 2 tablespoons meadowsweet aerial parts and ½ cup just-off-the-boil distilled water, steep for 15 minutes covered, and strain. Measure out ⅓ cup and add aloe gel. If using a natural preservative that needs to be added to the water phase, add now and stir well; otherwise, wait until after cream has emulsified.

Place infused oil, mango butter, and beeswax in a double boiler over low heat (or glass bowl over a saucepan of simmering water) until beeswax and mango butter have melted and all ingredients are thoroughly combined. Remove from heat and transfer to a blender or a bowl (if using immersion blender) to cool.

Once oil mixture has cooled to room temperature and looks creamy and semi-solid, add vitamin E oil.

Turning blender on low-medium setting or using an immersion blender in a bowl, slowly add meadowsweet mixture to oil mixture while blending. Mixture will begin to emulsify and become creamy. Avoid overmixing. Cream will set up a bit more as it cools.

Pour cream into sterilized glass jars, label, and store in the refrigerator for 1-2 weeks (if using a preservative, shelf life will be longer).

This recipe is inspired by a clinical trial (Dobrev, 2007) on a saw palmetto-based preparation that was demonstrated to have a sebum-regulating effect. This daily moisturizer also includes anti-inflammatory meadowsweet and aloe, along with an optional antimicrobial essential oil. Omit essential oil for extra sensitive skin. If using the heated method to make the saw palmetto oil infusion, use jojoba oil instead of argan oil.

# Green Tea
## AND ROSE FACIAL CREAM

*Adapted from* Alchemy of Herbs *by Rosalee de la Foret* (*de la Foret. 2017*).

This gorgeous moisturizing cream is feather light yet nourishing to the skin and may just become a favorite in your skin care regimen! It makes a big batch, so either plan to halve the batch or make a full batch to share as gifts.

---

## INGREDIENTS

1 cup (8 fl oz) jojoba oil

3 tbsp green tea (*Camellia sinensis*) leaf

⅓ cup rose (*Rosa* spp.) petal

3 tbsp beeswax

2½ tbsp (1.3 fl oz) coconut oil

2 tbsp shea butter

⅓ cup (2.7 fl oz) rose (*Rosa* spp.) hydrosol

⅓ cup (2.7 fl oz) aloe (*Aloe vera*) leaf gel

½ tsp vitamin E oil

Natural preservative (optional)

## DIRECTIONS

Make the green tea- and rose-infused oil using the instructions in the herb-infused oil tutorial. Once you finish infusing and straining the oil, you should have ¾ cup infused oil. If you don't have ¾ cup, make up the difference by adding plain jojoba oil.

Place beeswax, coconut oil, and shea butter in a double boiler over low heat (or a glass or ceramic bowl or canning jar over a small saucepan of simmering water) until they have melted. Add the green tea- and rose-infused jojoba oil and stir until all ingredients are thoroughly combined and melted. Remove from heat and transfer to a blender or a bowl (if using immersion blender) to cool.

Meanwhile, combine the rose hydrosol and aloe gel. If using a natural preservative that needs to be added to the water phase, add now and stir well; otherwise, wait until after cream has emulsified.

Once oil mixture has cooled to room temperature and looks creamy and semi-solid, add vitamin E oil.

Turning blender on low-medium setting or using an immersion blender in a bowl, slowly add hydrosol mixture to oil mixture while blending. Mixture will begin to emulsify and become creamy. Avoid overmixing. Cream will set up a bit more as it cools.

Pour cream into sterilized glass jars, label, and store in the refrigerator for 1-2 weeks (if using a preservative, shelf life will be longer).

# Gentle Floral
# Skin Cream

A lovely floral treat for sensitive skin! If using the heated method to make the calendula oil infusion, use jojoba oil instead of argan oil.

## INGREDIENTS

¼ cup (2 fl oz) calendula (*Calendula officinalis*) flower-infused argan oil

2½ tbsp mango butter

1 tbsp beeswax

½ tsp vitamin E oil

¼ cup (2 fl oz) geranium (*Pelargonium* spp.) hydrosol

2½ tbsp (1.25 fl oz) aloe (*Aloe vera*) leaf gel

Natural preservative (optional)

## DIRECTIONS

Make the calendula-infused oil using the instructions in the herb-infused oil tutorial. Note that ¼ cup is the amount of finished herbal oil to include in the recipe—you may need to start with more oil when making the herb-infused oil, as the herbs will soak up some of the oil (if you forget to do this, just top off with some plain oil as needed for this recipe).

Place infused oil, mango butter, and beeswax in a double boiler or in a bowl in a saucepan filled with water over low heat (or glass bowl over a saucepan of simmering water) until

beeswax and mango butter have melted and ingredients are well-blended. Remove from heat and transfer to a blender or a bowl (if using immersion blender) to cool.

Stir hydrosol and aloe gel together. If using a natural preservative that needs to be added to the water phase, add now and stir well; otherwise, wait until after cream has emulsified.

Once oil mixture has cooled to room temperature and looks creamy and semi-solid, add vitamin E oil.

Turning blender on low-medium setting or using an immersion blender in a bowl, slowly add hydrosol mixture to oil mixture while blending. Mixture will begin to emulsify and become creamy. Avoid overmixing. Cream will set up a bit more as it cools.

Pour cream into sterilized glass jars, label, and store in the refrigerator for 1-2 weeks (if using a preservative, shelf life will be longer).

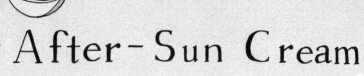

# After-Sun Cream

## INGREDIENTS

6 tbsp (3 fl oz) apricot oil infused with tulsi (*Ocimum tenuiflorum*) aerial parts

2 tbsp mango butter

½ tbsp beeswax

¼ cup (2 fl oz) aloe (*Aloe vera*) leaf gel

¼ cup (2 fl oz) rose (*Rosa* spp.) petal infusion

Natural preservative (optional)

---

This decadent, anti-inflammatory, and antioxidant cream is lovely any time of year, but is particularly beneficial for sun-exposed skin.

## DIRECTIONS

Make the tulsi-infused oil using the instructions in the herb-infused oil tutorial. Note that 6 tablespoons is the amount of finished herbal oil to include in the recipe — you may need to start with more oil when making the herb-infused oil, as the herbs will soak up some of the oil (if you forget to do this, just top off with some plain oil as needed for this recipe).

To prepare the rose infusion, combine 2 tablespoons rose petals and ½ cup just-off-the-boil water, steep for 15 minutes covered, and strain.

Place oil, mango butter, and beeswax in a double boiler over low heat (or glass bowl over a saucepan of simmering water) until beeswax and mango butter have melted and all ingredients are thoroughly combined. Remove from heat and let cool to room temperature, or until the edges of the mixture just begin to harden.

Meanwhile, combine ¼ cup rose infusion and aloe gel in a blender. If using a natural preservative that needs to be added to the water phase, add now and stir well; otherwise, wait until after cream has emulsified.

Turn blender on highest speed (with infusion and aloe gel still in it), and slowly pour in the oil mixture.

The emulsion should begin to harden after ⅔ of the oil/wax mixture has been added to the water; continue adding the oil/wax mixture until it is all incorporated.

Once the cream is silky and smooth, turn off the blender. Avoid overmixing.

Pour cream into sterilized glass jars, label, and store in the refrigerator for 1-2 weeks (shelf life will be longer if using a preservative).

# Richly Rosey Lotion

*Adapted from* Jeanne Rose's Kitchen Cosmetics *by Jeanne Rose (Rose, 1990).*

The rich scent of rose is a nice accompaniment to this silky smooth lotion.

## INGREDIENTS

1¼ cups (10 fl oz) sweet almond oil

¼ cup (2 fl oz) rose (*Rosa* spp.) hydrosol

5 tsp beeswax

¾ tsp vitamin E oil

5 drops rose (*Rosa* spp.) essential oil (optional)

Natural preservative (optional)

## DIRECTIONS

Combine the sweet almond oil and beeswax in a double boiler or in a bowl in a saucepan filled with water over low heat (or glass bowl over a saucepan of simmering water), stirring occasionally until completely melted.

Remove the oil/wax mixture from heat and allow to cool until the edges just begin to harden.

Pour into a clean, dry blender.

Measure out rose hydrosol. If using a natural preservative that needs to be added to the water phase, add now and stir well; otherwise, wait until after lotion has emulsified.

Turn the blender to medium-high speed.

Add rose hydrosol very slowly in a thin stream. The emulsion will begin to thicken and change color.

Add the vitamin E oil and the essential oil while it is blending.

Pour quickly into sterilized glass jars or a lotion bottle, cap, and label.

Store in the refrigerator for 1-2 weeks (if using a preservative, shelf life will be longer).

# Oregon Grape Root
# & Plantain Cream

This recipe combines berberine-rich Oregon grape root with anti-inflammatory and vulnerary plantain, coconut, and aloe in a psoriasis-soothing cream.

### INGREDIENTS

⅓ cup (2.7 fl oz) plantain (*Plantago* spp.) leaf-infused moringa or olive oil

2½ tbsp (1.25 fl oz) coconut oil

2 tbsp beeswax

½ tsp vitamin E oil

⅓ cup (2.7 fl oz) well-strained Oregon grape (*Berberis aquifolium*) root decoction

2½ tbsp (1.25 fl oz) aloe (*Aloe vera*) leaf gel

45 drops tea tree (*Melaleuca alternifolia*) essential oil (optional)

Natural preservative (optional)

## DIRECTIONS

Make the plantain-infused oil using the instructions in the herb-infused oil tutorial. Note that ⅓ cup is the amount of finished herbal oil to include in the recipe—you may need to start with more oil when making the herb-infused oil, as the herbs will soak up some of the oil (if you forget to do this, just top off with some plain oil as needed for this recipe).

Make a decoction using 4 tablespoons Oregon grape root and 1 cup water, simmering 20-30 minutes. Let cool, then strain. Combine ⅓ cup of the decoction and aloe gel. If using a natural preservative that needs to be added to the water phase, add now and stir well; otherwise, wait until after cream has emulsified.

Place infused oil, coconut oil, and beeswax in a double boiler over low heat (or glass bowl over a saucepan of simmering water) until beeswax and coconut oil have melted and all ingredients are thoroughly combined. Remove from heat and transfer to a blender or a bowl (if using immersion blender) to cool.

Once oil mixture has cooled to room temperature and looks creamy and semi-solid, add vitamin E oil.

Turning blender on low-medium setting or using an immersion blender in a bowl, slowly add Oregon grape root decoction mixture to oil mixture while blending. Mixture will begin to emulsify and become creamy. Avoid overmixing. Cream will set up a bit more as it cools. Add essential oil if desired, and stir to combine.

Pour cream into sterilized glass jars, label, and store in the refrigerator for 1-2 weeks (if using a preservative, shelf life will be longer).

# Calming Chamomile
## CREAM

Licorice and chamomile make a lovely herbal team for topical anti-inflammatory support. Try this cream on rosacea-prone or sensitive skin, hives, or skin inflammation of any sort!

### INGREDIENTS

⅓ cup (2.7 fl oz) chamomile (*Matricaria chamomilla*) flower-infused jojoba oil

2½ tbsp (1.25 fl oz) coconut oil

2 tbsp beeswax

½ tsp vitamin E oil

⅓ cup (2.7 fl oz) well-strained licorice (*Glycyrrhiza glabra*) root decoction

2½ tbsp (1.25 fl oz) aloe (*Aloe vera*) leaf gel

45 drops chamomile (*Matricaria chamomilla*) flower essential oil (optional)

Natural preservative (optional)

## DIRECTIONS

Make the chamomile-infused oil using the instructions in the herb-infused oil tutorial. Note that ⅓ cup is the amount of finished herbal oil to include in the recipe—you may need to start with more oil when making the herb-infused oil, as the herbs will soak up some of the oil (if you forget to do this, just top off with some plain oil as needed for this recipe).

Make decoction using 4 tablespoons licorice root to 1 cup water, simmering 20-30 minutes. Let cool, then strain. Add aloe gel. If using a natural preservative that needs to be added to the water phase, add now and stir well; otherwise, wait until after cream has emulsified.

Place infused oil, coconut oil, and beeswax in a double boiler over low heat (or glass bowl over a saucepan of simmering water) until beeswax and coconut oil have melted. Stir to blend. Remove from heat and transfer to a blender or a bowl (if using immersion blender) to cool.

Once oil mixture has cooled to room temperature and looks creamy and semi-solid, add vitamin E oil.

Blending on low-medium setting or using an immersion blender in a bowl, slowly add licorice decoction mixture to oil mixture while blending. Mixture will begin to emulsify and become creamy. Avoid overmixing. Cream will set up a bit more as it cools. Add essential oil and stir to combine.

Pour cream into sterilized glass jars, label, and store in the refrigerator for 1-2 weeks (if using a preservative, shelf life will be longer).

# Chickweed &
# CALENDULA CREAM

Chickweed is itchy skin's best friend, and along with calendula, sesame oil, and cocoa butter, can help to ease the irritation of eczema. Using fresh chickweed juice is optimal in this recipe, but if you don't have access to fresh chickweed, a dried herb infusion will do the trick.

## INGREDIENTS

⅓ cup (2.7 fl oz) calendula (*Calendula officinalis*)
flower-infused sesame oil

2 ½ tbsp cocoa butter

2 tbsp beeswax

½ tsp vitamin E oil

⅓ cup (2.7 fl oz) chickweed (*Stellaria media*)
aboveground parts juice or
dried chickweed infusion made with distilled water

Natural preservative (optional)

## DIRECTIONS

Make the calendula-infused oil using the instructions in the herb-infused oil tutorial. Note that ⅓ cup is the amount of finished herbal oil to include in the recipe. you may need to start with more oil when making the herb-infused oil. as the herbs will soak up some of the oil (if you forget to do this. just top off with some plain oil as needed for this recipe).

Extract chickweed juice with a juicer or by blending a bit more than ½ cup distilled water with a couple handfuls of fresh chickweed and straining through cheesecloth; alternatively, prepare the chickweed infusion by combining 2 tablespoons chickweed aerial parts and ½ cup just-off-the-boil distilled water, steep for 15 minutes covered, and strain. If using a natural preservative that needs to be added to the water phase, add now and stir well; otherwise, wait until after cream has emulsified.

Place oil, cocoa butter, and beeswax in a double boiler over low heat (or glass bowl over a saucepan of simmering water) until beeswax and cocoa butter have melted and all ingredients are thoroughly combined.

Remove from heat and transfer to a blender or a bowl (if using immersion blender) to cool.

Once oil mixture has cooled to room temperature and looks creamy and semi-solid, add vitamin E oil.

Turning blender on low-medium setting or using an immersion blender in a bowl, slowly add ⅓ cup chickweed juice or infusion to oil mixture while blending.

Mixture will begin to emulsify and become creamy.

Avoid overmixing. Cream will set up a bit more as it cools.

Pour cream into sterilized glass jars, label, and store in the refrigerator for 1-2 weeks (if using a preservative, shelf life will be longer).

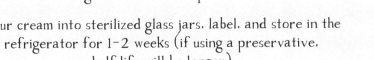

# SELF HEAL AND HONEY
## Shaving Cream

*Adapted from Kelly Cable (Cable. 2014).*

### INGREDIENTS

½ cup (4 fl oz) self heal (*Prunella vulgaris*) aerial parts-infused sweet almond oil (plantain (*Plantago* spp.) leaf can be used if self heal is unavailable)

¼ cup mango or cocoa butter

¼ cup (2 fl oz) castile soap

¼ cup (2 fl oz) raw honey

10 drops essential oil of choice (optional)

Natural preservative (optional)

Distilled water (optional)

### DIRECTIONS

Make the self heal-infused sweet almond oil using the instructions in the herb-infused oil tutorial. Note that ½ cup is the amount of finished herbal oil to include in the recipe—you may need to start with more oil when making the herb-infused oil, as the herbs will soak up some of the oil (if you forget to do this, just top off with some plain oil as needed for this recipe).

Gently heat mango butter and infused herbal oil in a double boiler (or a glass or ceramic bowl or canning jar over a small saucepan of simmering water) until mango butter is melted. Remove from heat and let cool slightly.

Add soap and honey to oil mixture. Once cooled to room temperature, add essential oil and if using, natural preservative, and stir to combine.

Pour into a 16-ounce bottle with foam-top and add enough distilled water to fill the bottle, and shake to combine. Store in the refrigerator for 1-2 weeks (if using a preservative, shelf life will be longer). Alternatively, skip the water to create a thicker shaving cream and extend shelf life.

Shake well before using.

This soothing shaving cream can be combined with water and dispensed from a foam-top bottle, or kept at a lotion-like consistency for extra moisture and a longer shelf life.

# Regenerating Floral
## FACE CREAM

*Adapted from* Organic Body Care Recipes *by Stephanie Tourles (Tourles, 2007).*

## INGREDIENTS

¼ cup (2 fl oz) sweet almond or macadamia oil

4 tsp rosehip seed oil

3 tsp beeswax

2 tbsp (1 fl oz) geranium (*Pelargonium* spp.) or neroli (*Citrus* x *aurantium*) hydrosol

¼ tsp vitamin E oil

20 drops lavender (*Lavandula* spp.) or rose geranium (*Pelargonium graveolens*) essential oil, 20 drops neroli (*Citrus aurantium*) essential oil, and 10 drops ylang ylang (*Cananga odorata*) essential oil (optional)

Natural preservative (optional)

## DIRECTIONS

Gently heat oils and beeswax in a double boiler (or a glass or ceramic bowl or canning jar over a small saucepan of simmering water) until melted. Stir thoroughly to ensure ingredients are well-blended. Remove from heat and allow to cool.

Once oil mixture has come to room temperature and looks semi-solid, stir in vitamin E oil.

If using a natural preservative that needs to be added to the water phase, add now to hydrosol and stir well; otherwise, wait until after cream has emulsified.

Using an immersion blender or hand mixer, gradually add the hydrosol to the oil and wax mixture in a thin stream until mixture becomes white and creamy. Avoid overmixing. Stir in essential oils.

Pour into sterilized jars or bottles and label. Store in the refrigerator for 1-2 weeks (if using a preservative, shelf life will be longer).

This lovely, skin-regenerating cream is a floral feast for the skin!

117

# BABY
## LOTION

A light, moisturizing lotion with soothing and uplifting lemon balm to delight the senses—gentle enough for baby, but loved by all!

## INGREDIENTS

½ cup (4 fl oz)
lemon balm
(*Melissa officinalis*)
hydrosol

6 tbsp (3 fl oz) sweet
almond oil infused with
lavender
(*Lavandula* spp.)
flower bud

½ tbsp beeswax

Natural preservative
(optional)

## DIRECTIONS

Pour hydrosol into a blender. If using a natural preservative that needs to be added to the water phase, add now and stir well; otherwise, wait until after lotion has emulsified.

Combine sweet almond oil and beeswax in a double boiler over low heat (or a glass or ceramic bowl or canning jar over a small saucepan of simmering water), stirring occasionally until completely melted.

Remove the oil/wax mixture from the heat, and set aside, letting it cool for several minutes until the edges of the mixture begin to harden.

Turn the blender on high speed and slowly add the oil/wax mixture.

The emulsion should begin to harden after ⅔ of the oil/wax mixture has been added to the water; continue adding the oil/wax mixture until it is all incorporated.

Toward the end of the emulsification process, the sides of the blender may occasionally need to be scraped. To do this, turn off the blender momentarily.

Once the lotion is silky and smooth, turn off the blender.

Pour the lotion into sterilized jars, label, and store in the refrigerator for 1–2 weeks (if using a preservative, shelf life will be longer).

# Mediterranean Garden
# LOTION BARS

Step into your own private Mediterranean garden with this divinely scented and ultra-moisturizing lotion bar.

## INGREDIENTS

¼ cup (2 fl oz) apricot or olive oil infused with lavender (*Lavandula* spp.) flower bud

¼ cup shea butter

¼ cup beeswax

2 tbsp (1 fl oz) coconut oil

15 drops bergamot (*Citrus* x *bergamia*) essential oil, 10 drops lavender (*Lavandula* spp.) essential oil, and 10 drops clary sage (*Salvia sclarea*) essential oil (optional)

## DIRECTIONS

Make the lavender-infused oil using the instructions in the herb-infused oil tutorial. Note that ¼ cup is the amount of finished herbal oil to include in the recipe—you may need to start with more oil when making the herb-infused oil, as the herbs will soak up some of the oil (if you forget to do this, just top off with some plain oil as needed for this recipe).

Gently heat shea butter, beeswax, and coconut oil in a double boiler over low heat (or a glass or ceramic bowl or canning jar over a small saucepan of simmering water) until melted.

Add the lavender-infused olive oil and stir to combine.

Remove from heat, add essential oils if desired, and stir to combine.

Pour the warm, melted mixture into molds or small muffin tins (lined with parchment paper or muffin cups).

Allow to cool for at least 1 hour, remove from molds/tins, and store in a cool, dark place for up to 1 year.

# Honey Chamomile
## LOTION BARS

*Adapted from Mama Rosemary (Mama Rosemary, 2014).*

## INGREDIENTS

6 tbsp (3 fl oz) chamomile
(*Matricaria chamomilla*)
flower- and calendula
(*Calendula officinalis*)
flower-infused
grapeseed oil

½ cup beeswax

½ cup shea butter

1½ tsp raw honey

20-30 drops
essential oil(s)
of choice (optional)

---

Soothing and moisturizing
decadence for hands
and skin!

## DIRECTIONS

Make the chamomile- and calendula-infused oil using the instructions in the herb-infused oil tutorial. Note that 6 tablespoons is the amount of finished herbal oil to include in the recipe—you may need to start with more oil when making the herb-infused oil, as the herbs will soak up some of the oil (if you forget to do this, just top off with some plain oil as needed for this recipe).

Combine the herb-infused grapeseed oil, beeswax, and shea butter in a double boiler over low heat (or a glass or ceramic bowl or canning jar over a small saucepan of simmering water), stirring occasionally until completely melted. Once melted, remove from heat and stir in honey, being thorough to stir until honey is completely incorporated (or it is prone to separate in the lotion bar).

Add essential oils (if using) and stir to combine.

Pour mixture into molds. Bars will harden as they cool.

If honey does not stay mixed in the bar upon cooling, or if bar is too soft for your preference, gently remelt the bars and add a bit more beeswax.

Store in a cool, dark place for up to 1 year.

To use, rub a bar on the skin, letting the heat of your skin melt the lotion.

# Gotu Kola
# Lotion Bar

## INGREDIENTS

¼ cup (2 fl oz) gotu kola (*Centella asiatica*) leaf-infused olive oil

¼ cup mango or kukui nut butter

¼ cup shea butter

½ cup beeswax

1 tsp vitamin E oil

Gotu kola, well known in both ayurvedic medicine and Western herbalism for its ability to promote wound healing and repair damaged skin, is an excellent addition to a skin care routine for skin affected by psoriasis.

## DIRECTIONS

Make the gotu kola-infused oil using the instructions in the herb-infused oil tutorial. Note that ¼ cup is the amount of finished herbal oil to include in the recipe—you may need to start with more oil when making the herb-infused oil, as the herbs will soak up some of the oil (if you forget to do this, just top off with some plain oil as needed for this recipe).

Place mango butter, shea butter, and beeswax in a double boiler over low heat (or glass bowl over a saucepan of simmering water) until beeswax and butters have melted.

Add the gotu kola-infused oil. Continue to heat just briefly until all ingredients are melted together.

Remove from heat and cool for 1 minute, then stir in vitamin E oil.

Pour mixture into heat-proof silicone soap or candy molds.

Allow to cool completely.

Pop lotion bars out of the molds and store in tins or a jar, separated by layers of wax or parchment paper, in a cool, dark place. Don't forget to label!

To use, rub bar onto dry skin, letting the bar melt from the warmth of your body.

Store in a cool, dark place for up to 1 year.

# Itchy Skin
# LOTION BAR

Adapted from 101 Easy Homemade Products for Your Skin, Health,
& Home by Jan Berry (Berry. 2016a).

## INGREDIENTS

3 tbsp (1.5 fl oz)
calendula (*Calendula
officinalis*) flower-and
licorice (*Glycyrrhiza
glabra*) root-infused
grapeseed oil
(or other infused
herbal oil)

3 tbsp shea butter

5 tbsp beeswax

꙰

Calendula and
licorice combine to
soothe dry, itchy,
or irritated skin
in this easy-to-use
lotion bar. Apply to
irritated areas of
skin or use as an all-
over moisturizer for
dry, inflamed skin.

## DIRECTIONS

Make the calendula- and licorice-infused
oil using the instructions in the herb-infused
oil tutorial. Note that 3 tablespoons is the
amount of finished herbal oil to include in the
recipe—you may need to start with more
oil when making the herb-infused oil, as the
herbs will soak up some of the oil (if you
forget to do this, just top off with some plain
oil as needed for this recipe).

In a double boiler (or glass bowl over a
saucepan of simmering water), combine shea
butter and beeswax.

Heat over low-medium heat until beeswax is
melted, and then add the calendula-licorice
oil. Continue to heat just briefly until all
ingredients are melted together.

Pour mixture into heat-proof silicone soap
or candy molds. Allow to cool completely.

Pop lotion bars out of the molds and store in
tins or a jar, separated by layers of wax or
parchment paper, in a cool, dark place for
up to 1 year. Don't forget to label!

To use, rub bar onto dry skin, letting the bar
melt from the warmth of your body.

# *Bathed in Flowers*
## BODY BUTTER

### INGREDIENTS

2 tbsp beeswax

⅓ cup shea butter

⅔ cup (5.3 fl oz) extra virgin olive oil infused with your choice of gentle herbs such as calendula (*Calendula officinalis*) flower, elder (*Sambucus nigra* or *Sambucus canadensis*) flower, or chickweed (*Stellaria media*) aboveground parts, or a combination

½ tsp vitamin E oil

This makes a gentle, yet luxurious body butter. You can easily customize this body butter with your favorite skin herbs.

### DIRECTIONS

Make the herb-infused oil using the instructions in the herb-infused oil tutorial. Note that ⅔ cup is the amount of finished herbal oil to include in the recipe—you may need to start with more oil when making the herb-infused oil, as the herbs will soak up some of the oil (if you forget to do this, just top off with some plain oil as needed for this recipe).

Gently heat shea butter and beeswax in a double boiler over low heat (or a glass or ceramic bowl or canning jar over a small saucepan of simmering water) until melted. Add the herb-infused oil, stir until mixture is melted and consistent, and turn off the heat.

Let cool for approximately 10 minutes, and once it is still warm, but not hot to the touch, cover and transfer to the refrigerator for approximately 1 hour, or until there is no longer a semi-liquid center. Add vitamin E oil.

Using an immersion blender or electric mixer, whip the mixture on high for 5 minutes, until the mixture changes color and looks fluffy. You may need to periodically scrape the mixture from the sides of the bowl.

Pour body butter into sterilized glass jars, label, and store in the refrigerator for up to 1 year.

# Vanilla Whipped BODY BUTTER

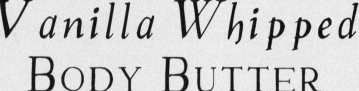

*Adapted from Plant-Powered Beauty by Amy Galper and Christina Daigneault (Galper & Daigneault. 2018).*

## INGREDIENTS

¼ cup (2 fl oz) coconut oil

¼ cup shea butter

¼ cup cocoa butter

¼ cup (2 fl oz) jojoba oil infused with vanilla (*Vanilla planifolia*) bean

35 drops sweet orange (*Citrus x sinensis*) essential oil and 5 drops ylang ylang (*Cananga odorata*) essential oil (optional)

The scent of this fluffy and decadent body butter is reminiscent of an orange creamsicle!

## DIRECTIONS

Make the vanilla-infused jojoba oil using the instructions in the herb-infused oil tutorial using ¼ vanilla bean and ¼ cup jojoba oil. Note that ¼ cup is the amount of finished herbal oil to include in the recipe—you may need to start with more oil when making the herb-infused oil, as the herbs will soak up some of the oil (if you forget to do this, just top off with some plain oil as needed for this recipe).

Gently heat coconut oil, shea butter, and cocoa butter in a double boiler over low heat (or a glass or ceramic bowl or canning jar over a small saucepan of simmering water) until melted.

Add the vanilla-infused jojoba oil, stir until mixture is melted and consistent, and turn off the heat.

Let cool for approximately 10 minutes, and once it is still warm, but not hot to the touch, cover and transfer to the refrigerator for approximately 1 hour, or until there is no longer a semi-liquid center.

Using an immersion blender or electric mixer, whip the mixture on high for 5 minutes or until it changes color and looks fluffy. You may need to periodically scrape the mixture from the sides of the bowl.

Add essential oil, if desired, and mix.

Label, and store in a cool, dark place. This recipe will keep for up to 1 year.

# Colloidal Oat
# BODY BUTTER

## INGREDIENTS

¼ cup shea butter

½ cup (4 fl oz) coconut oil

¼ cup colloidal oatmeal

½ tsp vitamin E oil

This recipe relies on colloidal oats; these are extremely finely powdered, so they stay in suspension. Although you can substitute oats that have been powdered at home in a coffee grinder or spice mill, they may leave your body butter with a slightly gritty texture and be more prone to separate, however, we've provided directions that will minimize that if using oat flour.

## DIRECTIONS

Combine the shea butter and coconut oil in a double boiler over low heat (or glass bowl over a saucepan of simmering water) and heat until completely melted.

Allow to cool slightly, then stir in the colloidal oats and vitamin E oil. Whisk everything together thoroughly until it forms a creamy mixture.

Allow the mixture to cool to room temperature, then give it a brief whirl with an immersion blender or stand mixer to give the cream a whipped texture. To keep the oats suspended in the cream (especially if using oat flour), cool further in the refrigerator until it's the consistency of very thick pancake batter; give it another few whirls with the immersion blender.

Dispense into small, sterilized jars for storage, and label. This cream will harden if stored in the refrigerator, but will soften up again when brought to room temperature. (Note: it will melt if exposed to warm temperatures.)

Store in a cool, dry place for up to 6 months.

# *Evergreen Forest*
# BODY BUTTER

Evergreen needles lend their antioxidant and antimicrobial
properties in this woodsy body butter. Any evergreen will do,
including the annual Christmas tree, but do avoid yew (*Taxus* spp.)
as they are toxic. Spruce, pine, and fir are all nice options, with
white fir (*Abies concolor*) being a particular favorite. If you choose
to add essential oils for scent, fir and pine are nice options. The
arrowroot powder makes the body butter a little less greasy, but is
optional; the recommended oils are those oils that are less greasy.

## INGREDIENTS

½ cup (4 fl oz) evergreen-infused herbal oil
(grapeseed, sunflower, sweet almond,
apricot kernel, or jojoba)

¼ cup shea butter

¼ cup mango butter (or more shea butter)

20-30 drops evergreen types of essential oil (optional)

¼ tsp arrowroot powder (optional)

## DIRECTIONS

Make the evergreen-infused herbal oil using the instructions
in the herb-infused oil tutorial. Note that ½ cup is the amount
of finished herbal oil to include in the recipe—you may need
to start with more oil when making the herb-infused oil, as the
herbs will soak up some of the oil (if you forget to do this, just
top off with some plain oil as needed for this recipe).

Gently heat shea and mango butter in a double boiler (or glass bowl over a saucepan of simmering water) until melted. Add the evergreen-infused oil, stir until mixture is melted and consistent, and turn off the heat.

Let cool for approximately 10 minutes, and once it is still warm, but not hot to the touch, cover and transfer to the refrigerator for approximately 1 hour, or until there is no longer a semi-liquid center.

Using an immersion blender or electric mixer, whip the mixture on high for 5 minutes, or until it changes color and looks fluffy. You may need to periodically scrape the mixture from the sides of the bowl.

Add essential oil, if desired, and mix.

Label, and store in a cool, dark place. This recipe will keep for up to 1 year.

# Chamomile
## BODY BUTTER

*Adapted from* 101 Easy Homemade Products for Your Skin, Health, & Home
*by Jan Berry (Berry. 2016a).*

## INGREDIENTS

½ cup (4 fl oz) chamomile (*Matricaria chamomilla*) flower-infused coconut oil

¼ cup shea butter

A few drops Roman chamomile (*Chamaemelum nobile*) essential oil

A skin-soothing body butter gentle enough for sensitive skin.

## DIRECTIONS

Make the chamomile-infused coconut oil using the instructions in the herb-infused oil tutorial. Note that ½ cup is the amount of finished herbal oil to include in the recipe—you may need to start with more oil when making the herb-infused oil, as the herbs will soak up some of the oil (if you forget to do this, just top off with some plain oil as needed for this recipe).

Gently heat shea butter in a double boiler over low heat (or a glass or ceramic bowl or canning jar over a small saucepan of simmering water) until melted. Add the chamomile-infused oil, stir until mixture is melted and consistent, and turn off the heat.

Let cool for approximately 10 minutes, and once it is still warm, but not hot to the touch, cover and transfer to the refrigerator for approximately 1 hour, or until there is no longer a semi-liquid center.

Using an immersion blender or electric mixer, whip the mixture on high for 5 minutes, or until it changes color and looks fluffy. You may need to periodically scrape the mixture from the sides of the bowl.

Add essential oil, if desired, and mix.

Label, and store in a cool, dark place. This recipe will keep for up to 1 year.

*The very act of creating and using homemade body care products is a self-care practice: you take time to evaluate your needs, gather ideas and ingredients, carefully combine and refine your formulas, and then treat yourself to the finished product as a reward!*

BOTANICAL SKIN CARE COURSE

CHAPTER EIGHT

# DEODORANTS

# DEODORANTS

Natural deodorants are gaining popularity as part of the growing green beauty industry, but it's simple and rewarding to make your own. We've got a range of deodorant recipes for you to try, from fresh sprays and wipes to clay-based deodorant balm. The best part of DIY deodorant is finding the natural herbal fragrance that's just right for your body, so mix and match oils and aromatic ingredients to find what you love!

# Bergamot
# DEODORANT

*Adapted from Davida Lederle (Lederle. 2017).*

Bergamot is an unexpected, but slightly seductive and versatile scent that lasts when the weather warms up. Add additional scents of your own design to personalize this recipe. This is a softer deodorant that works well for hand application.

## INGREDIENTS

2½ tbsp (1.25 fl oz) coconut oil

2½ tbsp shea butter

¼ cup arrowroot powder

2 tbsp baking soda

12 drops bergamot (*Citrus x bergamia*) essential oil

2-4 drops of your own signature essential oil

## DIRECTIONS

Gently heat coconut oil and shea butter in a double boiler (or a glass or ceramic bowl or canning jar over a small saucepan of simmering water) until melted. Stir to ensure a consistent mixture.

Add arrowroot powder, baking soda, and essential oils.

Place in a glass jar and allow to cool.

Cover with lid, label, and store in a cool, dark place for up to 1 year.

To apply, retrieve a small amount with a spoon or cotton swab, then rub into underarm area using fingers.

# Lavender Deodorant
## FOR SENSITIVE SKIN

*Adapted from Elise New (New. 2017).*

### INGREDIENTS

2 tbsp (1 fl oz) coconut oil

1 tbsp beeswax

1 tbsp shea butter

2 tbsp bentonite clay

1 tbsp baking soda

15 drops lavender (*Lavandula* spp.) essential oil

### DIRECTIONS

Combine the coconut oil, beeswax, and shea butter in a double boiler over low heat (or a glass or ceramic bowl or canning jar over a small saucepan of simmering water) and heat until completely melted.

Turn off the heat and stir in clay and baking soda.

Add essential oil.

Mix well.

Pour into a deodorant container and let cool before capping.

Label, and store in a cool, dark place for up to 1 year.

---

This gentle yet effective lavender deodorant goes on smoothly. The shea butter makes it a bit sticky, so it's best applied using a deodorant tube (as opposed to finger application).

# CHAMOMILE
## DEODORANT

*Adapted from Crunchy Betty (Crunchy Betty. 2019).*

---

This soothing deodorant really works! As a deodorant (as opposed to an antiperspirant), it doesn't stop sweating, but it does eliminate odor. If desired, substitute grapeseed or sweet almond oil for the sunflower oil, and lavender or tea tree essential oil for the chamomile essential oil.

## *INGREDIENTS*

### INFUSED OIL:

⅓ cup chamomile (*Matricaria chamomilla*) flower

¼ cup calendula (*Calendula officinalis*) flower

⅔ cup (5.3 fl oz) coconut oil

⅓ cup (2.7 fl oz) sunflower oil

### DEODORANT:

½ cup (4 fl oz) chamomile (*Matricaria chamomilla*) flower- and calendula (*Calendula officinalis*) flower-infused oil

6 tbsp baking soda

6 tbsp arrowroot powder

20 drops Roman chamomile (*Chamaemelum nobile*) essential oil

## DIRECTIONS

Following the directions for making an herb-infused oil,
infuse the chamomile and calendula into the combined coconut
and sunflower oils. To keep the coconut oil liquified, place jar
in a warm spot or infuse using the heat method. This recipe
will make enough infused oil for 2 batches of deodorant.

In a bowl, combine ½ cup of the strained, herb-infused oil
with the remaining ingredients, stirring well.

Transfer to a sterilized jar or jars and store in a cool,
dark place for up to 1 year.

To apply, retrieve a small amount with a spoon or cotton
swab, then rub into underarm area using fingers.

# Citrus + Pine
## DEODORANT SPRAY

*Adapted from* Grow Your Own Drugs *by James Wong (Wong, 2009).*

The resin of pine and other evergreen trees such as fir and spruce is antimicrobial, making it a natural fit for deodorant. Be sure to harvest only excess resin that has dripped below a wound in the tree bark, as the resin is the tree's own wound-healing mechanism.

## INGREDIENTS

2 tsp pine (*Pinus* spp.) or spruce (*Picea* spp.) resin

2 fresh lemon (*Citrus x limon*) peels, chopped

2 fresh orange or grapefruit (*Citrus* spp.) peels, chopped

10 fresh bay (*Laurus nobilis*) leaves, crushed

3 tbsp fresh pine (*Pinus* spp.) needle, chopped

3 tbsp fresh thyme (*Thymus vulgaris*) aerial parts

1 cup (8 fl oz) vodka

2 tbsp (1 fl oz) vegetable glycerin

½ cup (4 fl oz) neroli (*Citrus x aurantium*) hydrosol

Natural preservative (optional)

## DIRECTIONS

Place resin in the freezer to harden, which makes it easier to work with. Once frozen, crush resin into a powder in a mortar and pestle.

In a glass pint jar, combine resin, citrus peels, bay, pine, thyme, and vodka. Vodka should cover herbs by approximately 1 inch.

Cap and shake to combine. Place in a dark cupboard and infuse for 2–4 weeks.

When ready, strain the infused vodka through a fine mesh strainer.

Add glycerin and neroli hydrosol and mix thoroughly. Add natural preservative, if using.

Transfer to a glass spray bottle. Label, and store in a cool, dark place for up to 1 year.

To apply, shake well and spray on underarms.

# *Breezy Citrus* DEODORANT SPRAY

Unlike clay- or baking soda-based deodorant, you can easily mist this deodorizing spray on all sorts of sweaty spots where you might not want to spread a solid deodorant. This blend of scents is bright and refreshing, but you can certainly substitute other hydrosols or essential oil blends. Note that a thick aloe gel (not an aloe juice) is needed to serve as a carrier for the essential oils.

## INGREDIENTS

¼ cup (2 fl oz) witch hazel (*Hamamelis virginiana*) bark tincture (or commercial witch hazel extract)

¼ cup (2 fl oz) lemon balm (*Melissa officinalis*) or lemongrass (*Cymbopogon* spp.) hydrosol or distilled water

1 tbsp (0.5 fl oz) thick aloe (*Aloe vera*) leaf gel

10 drops clary sage (*Salvia sclarea*) essential oil

15 drops lemon (*Citrus x limon*) essential oil

Natural preservative (optional)

## DIRECTIONS

Combine thick aloe gel and essential oils in a small bowl, stirring well.

Add witch hazel, hydrosol, and and if using, natural preservative, whisk gently to combine.

Transfer to a 4-ounce bottle with spray top and shake well to combine.

Label, and store in a cool, dark place for 6-12 months (if using a preservative, shelf life will be longer).

Mist as needed on underarms, torso, legs, or feet. Although this could be used on the face for oily skin, it's likely to be quite drying, and you definitely don't want to spray this in your eyes!

# DEODORIZING WIPES

## INGREDIENTS

2 cups (16 fl oz) apple cider vinegar

1 cup lavender (*Lavandula* spp.) flower bud, peppermint (*Mentha x piperita*) leaf, lemon verbena (*Aloysia citrodora*) leaf, rose (*Rosa* spp.) petal, or any other herb or herbal combination that you enjoy the smell of!

---

Don't worry, these apple cider vinegar-based deodorizing wipes won't leave you smelling like vinegar—the vinegar smell dissipates soon after application!

## DIRECTIONS

Combine herbs in a quart-size glass jar.

Pour apple cider vinegar over the herbs, ensuring that the vinegar is covering the herbs by at least 1 inch.

Place a square piece of natural waxed paper on top of the jar, then seal the jar with a lid (this protects the extract from any chemical coating that may be on the lid, and protects the lid from rusting when using vinegar).

Cap tightly and give a shake to ensure that the herbs and menstruum are thoroughly mixed.

Label the jar, store in a cool, dark location, and visit every 1–3 days, giving the jar a shake. Add a bit more vinegar if needed to keep herbs covered after they initially absorb some of the vinegar.

Let macerate for 4–6 weeks.

Line a wire strainer with a few layers of cheesecloth, or simply place the cheesecloth within a funnel placed in the mouth of a jar, and decant the mixture.

Strain the mixture through the cheesecloth and with clean, dry hands, gather the cloth up and squeeze strongly, squeezing as much liquid from the herbs as possible.

Pour the liquid into a storage container full of thick paper towels or clean, cotton flannel cut into squares.

Keep in the refrigerator for up to 6 months and use wipes as needed to deodorize feet, armpits, etc.

These wipes can be stored in a plastic bag or cloth wet bag for up to 24 hours to use them on the go.

# No Baking Soda! DEODORANT

*Adapted from LisaLise (LisaLise. 2018).*

## INGREDIENTS

1½ tbsp beeswax

1 tbsp cocoa butter

2 tbsp shea butter

4 tbsp white kaolin clay

10 drops lavender (*Lavandula* spp.) essential oil

10 drops tea tree (*Melaleuca alternifolia*) essential oil

## DIRECTIONS

Gently heat beeswax and cocoa butter in a double boiler over low heat (or a glass or ceramic bowl or canning jar over a small saucepan of simmering water) until melted.

Add shea butter and stir until melted.

Add kaolin clay and stir until combined and smooth.

Remove from heat and add essential oils, stirring thoroughly. Note that this sets up and hardens quickly, so you'll want to be ready to pour it immediately once you remove it from the heat and add the essential oils.

Pour mixture into deodorant tubes and let set.

Label, and store in a cool, dark place for up to 1 year.

๛

This gentle but effective deodorant utilizes clay instead of baking soda, cornstarch, or arrowroot powder, which can be irritating to sensitive skin. Since this is a hard deodorant, it is best stored in a push-up deodorant container for easiest application; while the warmth of the skin will melt it on contact, a no-finger application works best with its waxy nature.

CHAPTER NINE

# GELS

# GELS

If you've tried soaking chia or flax seeds overnight, or if you've made a cold infusion of marshmallow (*Althaea officinalis*) root, you know all about the slippery, slimy, and soothing potency of herbal gels!

Herbal gels, gums, and mucilages can be used to help blend and thicken your herbal products and to help soothe irritated and inflamed skin and mucous membranes. Whether you're looking for an ultra-rich facial serum or a simple ointment to add to your first aid kit, learning to make your own herbal gels brings a whole new dimension to your herbal repertoire.

# Marshmallow + Chamomile
# Cooling Gel

Cooling aloe and marshmallow root infusion are a soothing base for hot skin conditions. Note that a thick aloe gel (not an aloe juice) is needed to serve as a carrier if essential oil is included in the recipe. Instead of Roman chamomile essential oil, you can use German chamomile (*Matricaria chamomilla*) essential oil, which will turn this gel a lovely blue color!

## INGREDIENTS

2 tbsp (1 fl oz) cold infusion of marshmallow
(*Althaea officinalis*) root, chilled

3 tbsp (1.5 fl oz) thick aloe (*Aloe vera*) leaf gel

10 drops Roman chamomile (*Chamaemelum nobile*)
essential oil

Natural preservative (optional)

## DIRECTIONS

Prepare the marshmallow infusion by combining 2 tablespoons marshmallow root and ½ cup cold water, then steeping in the refrigerator overnight.

Whisk aloe gel and essential oil together in a small bowl until thoroughly combined or blend with a hand mixer. Add marshmallow root infusion and whisk again.

Use right away, or label and store in refrigerator for up to 3 days (if using a preservative, shelf life will be longer).

Apply a thin layer to affected skin as needed.

# AFTER-SUN GEL

A wonderful preparation for the sun-loving herbal gardener and explorer, this gel is best kept in the refrigerator to increase its cooling effect. Use on sunburns and other types of burns.

## INGREDIENTS

¼ cup (2 fl oz) lavender (*Lavandula* spp.) hydrosol

¼ cup (2 fl oz) thick aloe (*Aloe vera*) leaf gel

¼ tsp xanthan gum

48 drops lavender (*Lavandula* spp.) essential oil

## DIRECTIONS

Using a glass measuring cup or 500-milliliter beaker, combine the lavender hydrosol and aloe gel, and stir until blended.

Add the xanthan gum, and mix with a mini hand mixer or immersion blender. To avoid clumping, sprinkle a little bit of the xanthan gum on the surface of the liquid at a time, mixing in between additions.

Once the xanthan gum is fully dissolved, add the drops of lavender essential oil, stirring them in completely.

Transfer gel to a glass bottle, label, and store in the refrigerator for up to 3 months.

To use, apply a thin layer to skin.

# Lavender and Aloe Gel

There's nothing more soothing than covering a burn with aloe gel—the ultimate cooling burn support. Lavender is also a traditional go-to for burns, with its anti-inflammatory, antioxidant, and vulnerary properties. Keep a jar of this lavender and aloe gel in your first aid kit for burns and sunburn.

## INGREDIENTS

¼ cup (2 fl oz) thick aloe (*Aloe vera*) leaf gel

15 drops lavender (*Lavandula* spp.) essential oil

## DIRECTIONS

Fill a 2-ounce glass jar with aloe gel and stir in essential oil.

Label, and store in a cool, dark place for up to 1 year.

Apply to minor burns as needed.

143

# Blemish Gel

This pH-balancing gel is useful for blemishes, breakouts, and healthy, balanced skin tone.

## INGREDIENTS

3 tbsp (1.5 fl oz) geranium (*Pelargonium* spp.) hydrosol

2 tsp herbal vinegar (simple or compounded: calendula (*Calendula officinalis*) flower, nettle (*Urtica dioica*) leaf, horsetail (*Equisetum arvense*) leaf and stem and/or gotu kola (*Centella asiatica*) leaf are great options)

¼ tsp xanthan gum

## DIRECTIONS

Using a glass measuring cup or 50-milliliter beaker, combine the vinegar(s) and hydrosol, and stir until fully blended.

Add the xanthan gum, and mix with a mini hand mixer or immersion blender. To avoid clumping, sprinkle a little bit of the xanthan gum on the surface of the liquid at a time, mixing in between additions.

Transfer gel to a glass bottle, label, and store in the refrigerator for up to 3 months.

Use as a spot treatment, 15-minute mask, or face serum for skin blemishes.

# Plantain Gel

Plantain is often used as a drawing agent for stings and splinters; when combined with nourishing and emollient Irish moss, it also makes a rich and soothing gel that's perfect for dermatitis, bites, scrapes, scratches, and almost any other minor skin irritation you can think of!

## INGREDIENTS

¼ cup (2 fl oz) plantain (*Plantago* spp.) leaf tincture

1 tbsp Irish moss (*Chondrus crispus*) thallus powder or ¼ tsp xanthan gum

## DIRECTIONS

Using a glass measuring cup or 50-milliliter beaker, combine your ingredients and mix with a mini hand mixer or immersion blender.

Transfer gel to a glass bottle, label, and keep with your first aid supplies for up to 6 months.

144

# Anti-Itch Gel

*Adapted from Herbal Formularies for Health Professionals Vol. 1 by Jill Stansbury (Stansbury. 2018).*

Peppermint essential oil is a great antipruritic (eases itching), and in a carrier of anti-inflammatory aloe gel, resinous calendula and myrrh tinctures, and antimicrobial Oregon grape root tincture, makes a soothing gel for itchy insect bites or contact dermatitis.

## INGREDIENTS

2 tbsp (1 fl oz) thick aloe (*Aloe vera*) leaf gel

1½ tsp Oregon grape (*Berberis aquifolium*) root or barberry (*Berberis* spp.) root tincture

1 tsp calendula (*Calendula officinalis*) flower tincture

1 tsp myrrh (*Commiphora myrrha*) resin tincture

10 drops peppermint (*Mentha x piperita*) essential oil

5 drops lavender (*Lavandula* spp.) essential oil

## DIRECTIONS

Combine aloe gel and essential oils in a glass measuring cup with a spout. Stir well to combine. Add remaining ingredients and stir again.

Transfer to a 2-ounce glass bottle.

Label, and store in a cool, dark place for up to 1 year.

Shake well, and apply to itchy skin as needed.

# Aloe and Green Tea Gel

Both aloe and green tea are antiviral and vulnerary, and the astringent nature of green tea can help to dry cold sore blisters and inhibit replication of the herpes simplex virus. Lemon balm essential oil has well-studied antiviral properties as well.

## INGREDIENTS

¼ cup (2 fl oz) thick aloe (*Aloe vera*) leaf gel

1 tbsp green tea (*Camellia sinensis*) leaf powder

20 drops lemon balm (*Melissa officinalis*) essential oil (optional)

## DIRECTIONS

Fill a 2-ounce glass jar with aloe gel and stir in powder and essential oil.

Label, and store in a cool, dark place for up to 1 year.

Apply to cold sores as needed.

## CHAPTER TEN

# HAIR CARE PRODUCTS

# HAIR CARE PRODUCTS

There's a lot that goes into caring for and managing our manes, from shampoo (or not!) to conditioners, masks, and treatments. There are so many commercial hair products to choose from, and so many ingredients on the label to think about. Making your own washes, conditioners, and styling products takes just a little time up front, and pays off in spades with simple products that don't contain any concerning chemicals, won't damage your hair, and will leave you with healthy, happy locks!

# Honey-Cinnamon HIGHLIGHTS

Honey contains enzymes that, when combined with distilled water, can produce the lightening agent hydrogen peroxide. While it won't radically change the color of your locks, it can produce subtle warm highlights—and unlike bleaching agents, this doubles as a conditioning hair mask! Take note before you get started: this recipe requires a bit of time investment.

## INGREDIENTS

¼ cup (2 fl oz) raw honey (Manuka honey is ideal, but any raw honey will work.)

1 cup (8 fl oz) distilled water

½ tsp cinnamon (*Cinnamomum* spp.) powder (optional)

½ tsp cardamom (*Elettaria cardamomum*) powder (optional)

## DIRECTIONS

Mix honey and water and allow to stand for 1 hour to allow hydrogen peroxide to develop.

Stir in cinnamon and cardamom powder, if using, and allow to sit for 10 minutes or so to absorb. It's a good idea to try a patch test on your skin before using cinnamon, especially if you have sensitive skin.

Pour mixture into a clean, squeeze-top bottle. It will have a fairly runny consistency; if desired, you can add more cinnamon and cardamom to thicken it up, but just remember that cinnamon is a rubefacient that can irritate the skin. Apply the mixture to your hair and work it in from roots to ends or wherever you desire highlights. Because this is a natural highlighter, you don't need to worry about trying to pull out individual sections. It will be runny, so you may want to do this in the shower, or at least leaning over a sink!

If your hair is long enough, pin up or put it in a bun: cover with a shower or swim cap.

Leave in place for 1–2 hours, and as long as overnight.

Wash the honey out thoroughly with shampoo: follow with conditioner.

This treatment can be repeated to bring out more color.

148

# Coffee Hair Color

*Adapted from Ann Marie Gianni (Gianni, n.d.).*

### INGREDIENTS

1 cup (8 fl oz) strong coffee or *espresso*

2 cups (16 fl oz) conditioner

2 tbsp used coffee grounds

1 cup (8 fl oz) apple cider vinegar

### DIRECTIONS

Combine coffee, conditioner, and grounds in a pump or squeeze bottle.

Apply to hair, after shampooing, and allow to sit for at least 1 hour.

Rinse with apple cider vinegar.

Store unused portion in refrigerator for up to 3 days. Repeat daily for a few days for darkest results.

# Hibiscus Red Hair Color

*Adapted from Katie Wells (Wells, 2019a).*

### INGREDIENTS

½ cup calendula (*Calendula officinalis*) flower

2-4 tbsp hibiscus (*Hibiscus sabdariffa*) flower

2 cups (16 fl oz) water

### DIRECTIONS

Add herbs and 2 cups water to a saucepan. Bring to a boil and then lower heat to a simmer.

Simmer for 30-40 minutes.

Strain flowers and store "hair tea" in a clean, glass jar in the refrigerator for up to 48 hours.

Use as a final rinse after shampooing/conditioning hair and repeat daily until desired shade is achieved, after which an application every few days may be necessary to maintain color.

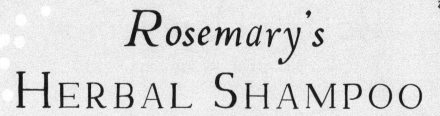

# *Rosemary's* HERBAL SHAMPOO

*Adapted from* Herbs for Natural Beauty *by Rosemary Gladstar (Gladstar. 2014).*

**A basic herbal shampoo that gets the job done!**

## INGREDIENTS

3 tbsp chamomile (*Matricaria chamomilla*) flower

3 tbsp rosemary (*Rosmarinus officinalis*) aerial parts

3 tbsp calendula (*Calendula officinalis*) flower

1 cup (8 fl oz) water

½ cup (4 fl oz) castile soap

¼ tsp jojoba oil or argan oil

20 drops essential oil of choice (optional)

Natural preservative (optional)

## DIRECTIONS

Place herbs in a heat-safe glass jar. Pour 1 cup just-off-the-boil water over herbs, cover, and let steep until it reaches room temperature.

Strain the tea and compost the herbs.

Add castile soap and mix gently.

Dilute essential oil (if using) in jojoba or argan oil and add to the mixture.

Transfer to a flip-top bottle and store in refrigerator between uses for up to 1 week (if using a preservative, shelf life will be longer).

# *Shampoo for* OILY HAIR

*Adapted from* Herbal Body Book *by Jeanne Rose* (*Rose. 2000*).

## INGREDIENTS

¼ cup lemongrass (*Cymbopogon* spp.) stalk

¼ cup willow (*Salix nigra*) bark

¼ cup peppermint (*Mentha* x *piperita*) leaf

1¼ cup (10 fl oz) water

2 tbsp (1 fl oz) castile soap

Natural preservative (optional)

## DIRECTIONS

Simmer herbs in 1¼ cup water for 10 minutes. Remove from heat and allow to infuse for an additional 10 minutes.

Strain liquid into an 8-ounce dark-colored glass bottle containing castile soap. Label, and store in the refrigerator.

Shake well and use as a shampoo.

If kept refrigerated, this will keep for 1 week (if using a preservative, shelf life will be longer).

⁎

Oily hair or scalp can benefit from the stimulating and astringent herbs in this simple-to-make shampoo.

# Dry Shampoo

This dry powder shampoo is a great quick option for neutralizing greasiness in the hair. For darker hair, choose rhassoul clay, which has a light brown color.

## INGREDIENTS

½ cup arrowroot powder

2 tbsp kaolin clay or rhassoul clay

1 tbsp rice powder (rice flour or finely ground and sifted rice)

## DIRECTIONS

Combine all ingredients in a bowl and whisk together.

Transfer to a sugar or salt shaker.

To use, sprinkle about 1 teaspoon of powder over scalp and hair; more or less can be used as needed. Carefully rub the dry shampoo in small amounts directly into the roots of the hair. Comb or brush through hair.

# Yucca Root
## SHAMPOO

*Adapted from* Herbs and Things *by Jeanne Rose* (Rose, 1972).

### INGREDIENTS

¼ cup cut and sifted yucca (*Yucca glauca*) root

2 cups (16 fl oz) water or rosemary (*Rosmarinus officinalis*), chamomile (*Matricaria chamomilla*), or lavender (*Lavandula* spp.) hydrosol

¼ cup (2 fl oz) (or less) castile soap (optional)

### DIRECTIONS

Boil ¼ cup cut and sifted yucca root in 2 cups of fresh water until it is reduced to 1 cup (powdered yucca root will be nearly impossible to strain out of the mixture).

Strain and cool.

Pour a small amount into your hands to test the lather with a little bit of water.

If you would like a more sudsy shampoo, add up to ¼ cup castile soap and mix to combine.

Store in refrigerator between uses and use within 1 week.

Jeanne Rose is an herbalist in the Southwest United States who has authored 22 books about herbs and aromatherapy. This is just one of her simpler recipes using a mucilaginous Southwest native plant to cleanse and deodorize the scalp. If you prefer to use a temperate region plant, marshmallow (*Althaea officinalis*) root will work similarly to yucca root—slippery, though not soapy.

# Herbal Lice Killer
## Shampoo Spray

*Adapted from Christina Anthis on the Herbal Academy blog (Anthis. 2014a).*

Avoid the insecticides used in common over-the-counter lice treatments with this lice-killing shampoo that is chock full of helpful herbs!

### INGREDIENTS

2 cups (16 fl oz) distilled water

10 whole soapnuts (*Sapindus* spp.), seeds removed,
or 20 prepared soapnut halves

2 tbsp dried orange (*Citrus* spp.) or lemon (*Citrus* x *limon*)
peel, or ¼ cup fresh peel

1 cinnamon (*Cinnamomum* spp.) stick

1 tbsp total thyme (*Thymus vulgaris*) aerial parts, sage
(*Salvia officinalis*) aerial parts, peppermint
(*Mentha* x *piperita*) leaf, rosemary (*Rosmarinus officinalis*)
aerial parts, lavender (*Lavandula* spp.) flower bud, lemongrass
(*Cymbopogon* spp.) stalk, and/or basil (*Ocimum basilicum*)
aerial parts, or 2 tbsp fresh herb

2 tbsp (1 fl oz) aloe (*Aloe vera*) leaf gel

2 tbsp (1 fl oz) apple cider vinegar

4 tbsp (2 fl oz) extra virgin olive oil

10 drops sweet orange (*Citrus* x *sinensis*) essential oil (for
children 2-6, use 1 drop; 6 and up use 5 drops)

5 drops tea tree (*Melaleuca alternifolia*) essential oil (for
children 2-6, use 1 drop; 6 and up use 3 drops)

9 drops cinnamon (*Cinnamomum* spp.) leaf essential oil (for
children 2-6, use 1 drop; 6 and up use 4 drops)

## DIRECTIONS

Place water, soapnuts, citrus peel, and cinnamon in a small pot; cover and bring to a boil. Reduce heat and simmer for 20 minutes.

Remove from heat and add dry herbs; allow to steep for about an hour, or until the liquid comes to room temperature. Strain and discard herbs.

Combine the infusion with all other ingredients in a spray bottle, label, and shake well.

To use, spray over hair and scalp until thoroughly saturated; cover with a shower cap or plastic wrap and leave in place for 1-4 hours.

Rinse hair well and comb thoroughly using a lice comb. Be careful not to get shampoo in the eyes.

Repeat daily; on repeat applications, the spray doesn't need to remain in place for as long—15 minutes is enough.

For best results, apply daily for a total of 8 consecutive days; this should be long enough to remove all nits and adult lice.

Store unused shampoo in refrigerator for up to 1 week.

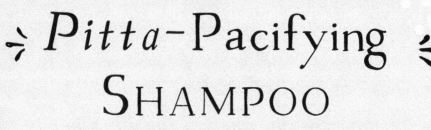

# Pitta-Pacifying
# SHAMPOO

*Adapted from* Enchanting Beauty
*by Manisha Kshirsagar (Kshirsagar, 2015).*

According to Ayurveda, high *pitta dosha* in the scalp and hair may result in premature greying or thinning, or an itching or burning scalp. Try this shampoo to cool *pitta*!

## INGREDIENTS

2 tsp peppermint (*Mentha* x *piperita*) leaf

1 tsp amalaki (*Phyllanthus emblica*) fruit powder

1 cup (8 fl oz) distilled water

¼ cup (2 fl oz) castile soap

Natural preservative (optional)

## DIRECTIONS

Combine herbs and water in a pot and bring to a boil.

Lower heat to a simmer and simmer for 10 minutes.

Remove from heat and allow to cool.

Strain the herbs from the liquid.

Combine the liquid with castile soap.

Bottle, label, and store in the refrigerator.

Shake well and use as shampoo.

If kept refrigerated, this will keep for 1 week
(if using a preservative, shelf life will be longer).

# *Henna Conditioner*
# FOR OILY HAIR

This recipe is specifically for individuals with oily skin and a scalp or hairline that is prone to blemishes. This is ideal for occasional use, especially if one has had to miss a shampooing and the scalp has grown oily and or irritated as a result. Henna is often called a natural conditioner, and is refreshing to oily skin. Zinc helps balance secretions of the sebaceous glands, while sage is astringent and antifungal. Note that zinc oxide powder poses some potential health risks if it's inhaled; be sure to use a dust mask when mixing the ingredients in this recipe.

## INGREDIENTS

1-4 tbsp henna
(*Lawsonia inermis*)
powder

¼ tsp zinc oxide
powder

1 tsp finely
powdered sage
(*Salvia officinalis*)
aerial parts

## DIRECTIONS

Measure 1 tablespoon henna powder per use to condition scalp area only or for short hair; use 2 tablespoons henna powder per use if you want to condition the entire length of the hair; for very long hair you may want to prepare 3 or 4 tablespoons of henna powder or more.

Add zinc oxide powder and sage and mix well.

Take the portion you will use and wet it to a thin paste with water or hydrosol.

Apply to problem areas of the scalp first, and then spread the remaining mixture over scalp and hair.

Let sit for 10-15 minutes or until the mixture starts to dry on the hair and scalp.

Rinse very thoroughly and towel off hair and scalp.

Comb the hair gently to encourage any remaining product to come loose from hair.

# Rose, Argan, & Coconut Shine

This moisturizing hair rinse for curly hair can be applied to wet hair as a conditioner, or dry hair as a shine.

### INGREDIENTS

½ cup (4 fl oz) argan oil

½ cup (4 fl oz) fractionated coconut oil

40 drops rose (*Rosa* spp.) essential oil

### DIRECTIONS

Pour combined oils into a dark-colored glass bottle or jar and add essential oil.

Cover, shake well, and label.

Use a small amount as needed on wet or dry hair.

Store in a cool, dark place for up to 1 year.

# Honey & Avocado Oil Treatment

The ultimate treat for curly hair—with only two ingredients from your kitchen!

### INGREDIENTS

¼ cup (2 fl oz) raw honey

¼ cup (2 fl oz) avocado oil or olive oil

### DIRECTIONS

Combine honey and oil in a bowl or jar and stir well to combine.

Apply to moist hair; leave in for at least 15 minutes.

Follow with curl-friendly shampoo or hair rinse.

# Ginger Sesame Oil

*Adapted from* The Herbs of Life: Health & Healing Using Western & Chinese Techniques *by Lesley Tierra (Tierra, 1992).*

According to both Chinese medicine and Ayurveda, dandruff may occur when there is insufficient blood supply to the scalp (Lad, 1998; Tierra, 1992). This mixture of sesame oil and ginger juice stimulates circulation and delivers nourishment to the dandruff-prone scalp.

## INGREDIENTS

2 tbsp (1 fl oz) sesame oil

2 tbsp (1 fl oz) fresh ginger
(*Zingiber officinale*) rhizome juice

## DIRECTIONS

Shred ginger and use a garlic press to extract juice (or just use a juicer!). Combine sesame oil and ginger juice in a small bottle or bowl and shake or whisk to combine.

Make as needed (do not store), and rub onto the scalp. Let sit on the scalp for at least 8 hours (place a shower cap or towel on your head and sleep while the ginger and sesame work their magic!).

Follow by washing with an herbal shampoo.

Repeat 2-3 times per week.

# Lice-Be-Gone
# HAIR OIL

This recipe calls for oil extracted from the seeds of the neem plant—although it certainly has a strong smell to it, this is not an essential oil! Neem is a common ingredient in head lice shampoos and has been used for centuries in ayurvedic medicine for a variety of skin infections, including lice (Pole, 2006).

## INGREDIENTS

½ cup (4 fl oz) neem oil

½ cup (4 fl oz) jojoba oil infused with thyme (*Thymus vulgaris*) aerial parts

1 tsp tea tree (*Melaleuca alternifolia*) essential oil

## DIRECTIONS

Prepare the thyme-infused jojoba oil using the instructions in the herb-infused oil tutorial. Note that ½ cup is the amount of finished herbal oil to include in the recipe—you may need to start with more oil when making the herb-infused oil, as the herbs will soak up some of the oil (if you forget to do this, just top off with some plain oil as needed for this recipe).

Combine oils in an 8-ounce dark-colored glass bottle. Cap, label, and store in a cool, dark place for up to 1 year.

To use, cover the hair and scalp with herbal oil after using a lice comb. Cover with a shower cap or plastic wrap and leave in place overnight.

Shampoo and then rinse with apple cider vinegar. For even more herbal action, use a vinegar infused with antimicrobial herbs such as thyme (*Thymus vulgaris*) aerial parts, rosemary (*Rosmarinus officinalis*) aerial parts, lavender (*Lavandula* spp.) flower bud, hyssop (*Hyssopus officinalis*) aerial parts, and/or yarrow (*Achillea millefolium*) aerial parts.

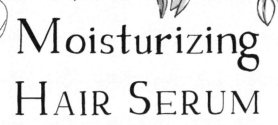

# Moisturizing
# HAIR SERUM

This deep conditioning oil is a treat for dry, thirsty hair. Geranium (*Pelargonium* spp.), lavender (*Lavandula* spp.), chamomile (*Matricaria chamomilla*), and rosemary (*Rosmarinus officinalis*, ct. 1,8 cineole or ct. verbenone) are nice essential oil options for normal to dry hair. If desired, you can also use herb-infused sweet almond or jojoba oil in place of the plain oil called for below.

## INGREDIENTS

2 tbsp (1 fl oz) sweet almond or olive oil

2 tbsp (1 fl oz) jojoba oil

1 tsp argan oil

⅛ tsp vitamin E oil

10 drops essential oil of choice

## DIRECTIONS

Combine all ingredients in a dark-colored glass bottle with a dropper top. Shake thoroughly to combine now and before each use.

Label, and store in a cool, dark place for up to 1 year.

To use, apply a few teaspoons of serum to wet hair during a bath or shower, making sure to use fingers to work it into the hair. Cover hair with a shower cap or plastic wrap, then wrap with a warm, damp towel, and let oil penetrate hair for at least 20 minutes and up to 1 hour. Shampoo thoroughly and rinse.

Alternatively, for a quicker application, rub 5–10 drops of herbal hair serum on the palms of your hands and then smooth hands throughout damp or dry hair, starting 2 inches below the root and down toward the end of the hair shaft.

# *Herbal*
# HAIR CLEANSING TEA

*Adapted from* Healing Herbal Infusions *by Colleen Codekas (Codekas. 2018).*

## INGREDIENTS

2 cups (16 fl oz) water

¼ cup sage (*Salvia officinalis*) aerial parts, fresh

¼ cup rosemary (*Rosmarinus officinalis*) aerial parts, fresh

¼ cup thyme (*Thymus vulgaris*) aerial parts, fresh

2 tbsp baking soda

## DIRECTIONS

Place herbs in a heat-safe glass jar. Pour 2 cups just-off-the-boil water over herbs, cover, and let steep until the infusion reaches room temperature.

Strain the tea and compost the herbs.

Add baking soda to tea and combine well.

Store in refrigerator between uses and use within 1 week.

Use 1-2 cups of hair cleansing tea 1-2 times per week.

Combines the benefits of an herbal hair rinse with the cleansing power of the baking soda "no 'poo" method. Other herbs to experiment with include calendula (*Calendula officinalis*) flower, chamomile (*Matricaria chamomilla*) flower, and yarrow (*Achillea millefolium*) aerial parts, which soothe the scalp and enhance highlights; lemon balm (*Melissa officinalis*) aerial parts and mint (*Mentha x piperita*) leaf, whose astringency can be helpful for oily hair; rosemary (*Rosmarinus officinalis*) aerial parts, mint (*Mentha x piperita*) leaf, ginger (*Zingiber officinale*) rhizome, and nettle (*Urtica dioica*) leaf to stimulate the scalp; black tea (*Camellia sinensis*) leaf and rosemary (*Rosmarinus officinalis*) aerial parts to darken hair; or nettle (*Urtica dioica*) leaf and yarrow (*Achillea millefolium*) aerial parts for dry, itchy dandruff.

# Herbal Vinegar
## DETANGLING RINSE

Apple cider vinegar restores pH balance to an itchy scalp and effectively detangles hair. The addition of moisturizing herbs adds a conditioning boost to benefit the hair. Don't worry, the vinegar smell fades once hair is dry!

### INGREDIENTS

4 cups (32 fl oz) apple cider vinegar

½ cup marshmallow (*Althaea officinalis*) root

½ cup calendula (*Calendula officinalis*) flower

½ cup nettle (*Urtica dioica*) leaf

½ cup violet (*Viola* spp.) aerial parts

### DIRECTIONS

Place herbs in a glass jar and cover with the vinegar. Place a piece of natural waxed paper between the jar and the lid, and seal. Set aside in a cool, dark cupboard for 2–4 weeks, shaking every few days.

Strain herbs from vinegar using a wire mesh strainer lined with cheesecloth or simply cheesecloth placed over a funnel. Squeeze herbs to release every last drop of vinegar.

Store herb-infused vinegar in a cool, dark place for up to 6 months. Don't forget to label!

To use, combine ¼ cup infused vinegar with ¾ cups water in a squirt bottle. Squirt onto scalp and work into hair thoroughly with fingers. (Since water will dilute the acidity of the vinegar and invite bacterial growth, making a big batch of vinegar and mixing only what you need each time removes any shelf-life concerns.)

Rinse with warm water.

Once the vinegar is mixed with water, the shelf life is just a few days, refrigerated.

# Comfrey Root
# DETANGLER

The ooey-gooey mucilage of comfrey root excels at detangling those dreaded knots! Marshmallow (*Althaea officinalis*) root can be used in place of comfrey.

## INGREDIENTS

4 tbsp comfrey (*Symphytum officinale*) root
or marshmallow (*Althaea officinalis*) root

3 cups (24 fl oz) water

½ tsp avocado, almond, or baobab oil

½ tsp vitamin E oil

Natural preservative (optional)

## DIRECTIONS

Make a comfrey decoction by simmering 4 tablespoons of comfrey root in 3 cups of uncovered water for 20–40 minutes. Alternatively, make a marshmallow root infusion by combining 4 tablespoons marshmallow root in 2 cups water, infusing overnight in the refrigerator.

Combine 1½ cups comfrey decoction or marshmallow infusion with oil and vitamin E in glass bottle or plastic squirt bottle.

Shake well to combine.

Store in refrigerator for up to 1 week (or add a preservative for longer shelf life).

To use, shake well, then use as a detangling rinse on wet hair in the shower. No need to rinse afterward, although you can if you like!

# Herbal Scalp Rinse
## *for Dandruff*

This recipe is a simple herbal infusion that includes cleavers (*Galium aparine*) aboveground parts, a mild vulnerary, astringent, and anti-inflammatory herb with an affinity for the skin that has a history of use as a hair rinse for dandruff (McIntyre, 2019).

## INGREDIENTS

¼ cup cleavers (*Galium aparine*) aboveground parts

¼ cup calendula (*Calendula officinalis*) flower

⅛ cup tulsi (*Ocimum tenuiflorum*) aerial parts

⅛ cup fenugreek (*Trigonella foenum-graecum*) seed

## DIRECTIONS

Make an infusion by adding herbs to a heat-safe quart-sized glass canning jar and pouring just-off-the-boil water over them to fill the jar. Cover and let steep for 4–8 hours.

Strain and store in the refrigerator for up to 24 hours.

Use as a hair rinse daily for 1–2 weeks.

# Anti-Dandruff
## Scalp Spray

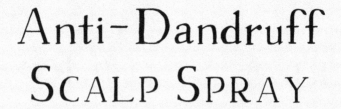

### INGREDIENTS

3 cups (24 fl oz) apple cider vinegar

½ cup fenugreek (*Trigonella foenum-graecum*) seed

¼ cup chickweed (*Stellaria media*) aboveground parts

¼ cup meadowsweet (*Filipendula ulmaria*) aerial parts

¼ cup oregano (*Origanum vulgare*) aerial parts

### DIRECTIONS

Combine herbs in a quart-size glass jar.

Pour apple cider vinegar over the herbs, ensuring that the vinegar is covering the herbs by at least 1 inch.

Place a square piece of natural waxed paper on top of the jar, then seal the jar with a lid (this protects the extract from any chemical coating that may be on the lid, and protects the lid from rusting when using vinegar).

Cap tightly and give a shake to ensure that the herbs and menstruum are thoroughly mixed.

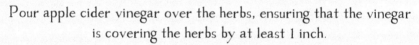

Label the jar, store in a cool, dark location, and visit every 1–3 days, giving the jar a shake. Add a bit more vinegar if needed to keep herbs covered after they initially absorb some of the vinegar.

Let macerate for 4–6 weeks.

Line a wire strainer with a few layers of cheesecloth, or simply place the cheesecloth within a funnel placed in the mouth of a jar,

and decant the mixture.

Strain the mixture through the cheesecloth and with clean, dry hands, gather the cloth up and squeeze strongly, squeezing as much liquid from the herbs as possible.

Transfer the liquid into a glass jar using a funnel.

Label, and store in a cool, dark place for up to 6 months.

To use this spray, mix equal parts herbal vinegar and water in a spray bottle. Spray on scalp after shampooing and let sit for 15 minutes. Rinse.

Use 2-3 times a week.

Antimicrobial, anti-inflammatory, and antipruritic herbs combine in this apple cider vinegar-based scalp spray. Keep this on hand for periods of dandruff, or any other itchy or irritated scalp condition!

# GERANIUM
# SCALP SPRAY

### INGREDIENTS

⅓ cup (2.7 fl oz) geranium
(*Pelargonium* spp.) hydrosol

½ cup (4 fl oz) calendula (*Calendula officinalis*)
flower infusion

3 tbsp (1.5 fl oz) apple cider vinegar

3 tbsp (1.5 fl oz) thick aloe (*Aloe vera*) leaf gel

10 drops geranium (*Pelargonium* spp.)
essential oil (optional)

Natural preservative (optional)

### DIRECTIONS

Combine ingredients in a jar and shake gently to blend.

Transfer to a spray or squeeze bottle, label, and store
in refrigerator for up to 1 week
(if using a preservative, shelf life will be longer).

Spray directly on scalp after washing and conditioning
hair or when scalp feels itchy or irritated.

This botanical spray is soothing to itchy or irritated scalps.
Note that thick aloe gel is needed as a carrier
for the essential oil.

# Shea & Clay
# HAIR TEXTURIZER

*Adapted from Roxie Hunt (Hunt. 2018).*

## INGREDIENTS

¼ cup shea butter

1 tbsp beeswax

1 tbsp myrrh
(*Commiphora myrrha*)
resin powder

1 tsp arrowroot powder

1 tsp bentonite clay

1 tsp baking soda

2–3 drops essential oil
(optional)

This powder-enhanced balm can be used to bring life to fine hair and can also be used as a mustache balm!

## DIRECTIONS

Combine the shea butter and beeswax in a double boiler over low heat (or a glass or ceramic bowl or canning jar over a small saucepan of simmering water), stirring occasionally until completely melted and combined. Remove from heat.

Place a flour sifter or tea strainer with very fine mesh over melted oil and beeswax mixture. The goal is to capture any larger particles of the myrrh resin powder, so very fine mesh is needed. Sift powdered ingredients into mixture. Stir until combined.

Add essential oil if desired, and stir again. If there are still particles from the myrrh resin in the mixture, use a very fine mesh filter when pouring melted mixture into the jar in the next step.

Pour into a glass jar, and set aside to cool.

Label, and store in a cool, dark place for up to 1 year.

To use, rub a small amount between palms and apply to hair for smooth style control.

# Natural
## ⊰ HAIR POMADE ⊱

*Adapted from Katie Vance (Vance. 2015).*

This recipe provides firm hold and boosts volume, but is still easy to wash out of the hair. A small amount goes a long way with this mixture, so apply sparingly. If you'd like more hold, increase the beeswax; for a softer hold, decrease the beeswax.

## INGREDIENTS

2 tbsp beeswax

2 tbsp coconut oil

2 tsp bentonite clay

10 drops essential oils of your choice (optional)

## DIRECTIONS

Heat beeswax and coconut oil in a double boiler over low heat (or a glass or ceramic bowl or canning jar over a small saucepan of simmering water) until beeswax is completely melted.

Remove from heat and immediately add the bentonite clay.

Gently stir the mixture as it cools.

Dip a clean spoon into the formula and place it into the refrigerator so it will cool quickly and you can determine if its consistency is what you desire. If the sample is too soft, add a little more wax to the warm pomade; if the sample is too hard, add a little more oil.

Add essential oils and stir again.

Pour into a container and let cool.

Cap and store in a cool, dark place for up to 1 year.

To use, rub a small amount between palms and apply to hair.

# Rosemary Hair Rinse

Rosemary boosts circulation to the scalp, and a rosemary hair rinse is a great alternative to shampoo if your hair feels dry, but your scalp feels greasy!

## INGREDIENTS

A handful of fresh rosemary (*Rosmarinus officinalis*) sprigs

1 tsp apple cider vinegar

4 cups (32 fl oz) water

## DIRECTIONS

Place rosemary sprigs in a pot, along with 4 cups of water.

Simmer for 15-20 minutes, covered.

Strain rosemary from water and let liquid cool to warm.

Add apple cider vinegar and apply to hair. No need to rinse!

Store any extra in refrigerator for up to 3 days.

# Clay Conditioning Mask

The minerals in bentonite clay benefit the hair and may encourage hair growth. It also helps to condition, soften, and reduce frizz. This clay conditioning mask encourages curl definition and shine.

## INGREDIENTS

2 tsp bentonite clay

3-5 tsp water or hydrosol of choice

1 tsp avocado oil

## DIRECTIONS

Place bentonite clay in a small bowl and moisten with water or hydrosol until you have a yogurt-like consistency.

Add oil and stir to combine.

Rub into wet hair, leave for 5 minutes, and rinse with water.

# ⇒ Natural ⇐
## HAIR SPRAY

*Adapted from Katie Wells (Wells. 2019c).*

This simple recipe uses just a few common household ingredients and gives surprisingly effective hold!

## INGREDIENTS

1½ cups (12 fl oz) filtered or distilled water

2 tbsp white sugar

1 tbsp (0.5 fl oz) high-proof alcohol (e.g., vodka)

1 tsp sea salt (optional, to add volume and texture)

Natural preservative (optional)

## DIRECTIONS

Create a simple syrup by boiling the water and sugar, whisking until the sugar granules are completely dissolved in the water. Add salt, if using, and stir to dissolve.

Remove from heat and cool to room temperature.

Add alcohol and if using, natural preservative.

Store in a spray bottle for up to 1 week (if using a preservative, shelf life will be longer).

Apply as desired.

# Yogurt and Honey
## HAIR MASK

Protein-rich yogurt and moisturizing honey combine to restore dull, dry locks.

## INGREDIENTS

½ cup (4 fl oz) yogurt

¼ cup (2 fl oz) raw honey

2 tbsp (1 fl oz) jojoba oil

## DIRECTIONS

Combine ingredients in a small bowl and stir thoroughly.

Apply to hair and cover with shower cap.

Let this moisturizing mask penetrate hair for at least 20 minutes.

Rinse with warm water, then shampoo hair as usual.

# Marshmallow
## and Flax Hair Gel

*Adapted from Millicent Sarah (Sarah, 2017).*

## INGREDIENTS

¾ cup flax seeds

½ cup marshmallow
(*Althaea officinalis*)
root

5 cups (40 fl oz) aloe
(*Aloe vera*) leaf juice

---

A recipe for enhancing
those wild curls, this is
a light-hold gel great for
twists and wash-and-go
curls. This makes a big
batch, so feel free to
halve amounts.

## DIRECTIONS

Combine marshmallow root with 1 cup of aloe
juice in a saucepan. Simmer for 15–30 minutes,
keeping a close eye on the decoction so the
aloe juice doesn't just boil away (a fair amount
of it gets absorbed by the marshmallow root).
Remove from heat and let cool.

Combine flax seeds with remaining aloe juice in
a saucepan. Simmer for 15–30 minutes, stirring
frequently; remove from heat and let cool.

Once cool, strain the two decoctions,
keeping them separate.

Combine the two decoctions in a glass jar
or plastic squeeze tube. If desired, you can
experiment with proportions to achieve your
desired consistency: the flax gel is much thicker
than the marshmallow gel and will result in a
stiffer, stronger hold. (Note that if you desire a
higher proportion of marshmallow decoction to
flax decoction, you could alter the proportions
of the 5 cups of aloe juice you use initially with
the flax seeds and marshmallow root.
Feel free to experiment!)

This product does not have a preservative
so is best kept in the refrigerator and used
within 1 month.

Discard any remaining strained decoction,
or freeze and save for your next batch.

# Double-Avocado
# Moisturizing Hair Mask

*Adapted from* 200 Tips, Techniques, and Recipes for Natural Beauty *by Shannon Buck (Buck, 2014).*

This ultra lush, protein-rich hair mask will have your hair lustrous, shiny, and red carpet-ready in under 1 hour!

### INGREDIENTS

1 tbsp (0.5 fl oz) avocado oil

½ avocado, mashed

2 egg yolks or 2 tbsp mayonnaise

10 drops lemon (*Citrus* x *limon*) or other essential oil (optional)

### DIRECTIONS

Combine all ingredients and mix well. The mixture has a fairly neutral smell; essential oil can be added for fragrance, if you like, but note that essential oils can be drying to the hair.

Apply to damp hair, working in sections; massage in from roots to ends.

Cover hair with a shower cap, or wrap your head in an old towel or t-shirt—it may get stained with oil, so use one you don't mind dedicating to hair wraps! Leave the hair mask in place for at least 10 minutes and up to 1 hour.

When you're ready to wash it out, start with a brief lukewarm rinse; the egg proteins in this mask will make your hair lustrous and shiny, but if you go straight for a hot rinse, they can make a bit of a mess—think scrambled eggs in your hair!

Follow with your usual gentle shampoo or conditioning wash.

# No 'Poo Hair Mud Mask

*Adapted from Christina Anthis (Anthis. 2014b).*

For some people, the ingredients in shampoos and conditioners can be too alkaline for the scalp, compromising the protective barrier created by the scalp's acid mantle. No 'Poo Hair Mud Mask is meant to maintain the pH balance of the scalp while also cleansing the hair.
Hair-friendly herbs include nettle (*Urtica dioica*) leaf, chamomile (*Matricaria chamomilla*) flower, horsetail (*Equisetum arvense*) leaf and stem, and rosemary (*Rosmarinus officinalis*) aerial parts.

## INGREDIENTS

2 cups (16 fl oz) filtered or distilled water

¼ cup marshmallow (*Althaea officinalis*) root

4-6 tbsp dried herbs of your choice

½ cup (4 fl oz) raw, unfiltered apple cider vinegar

¾ cup bentonite clay

¼ cup (4 fl oz) aloe (*Aloe vera*) leaf gel

1 tbsp (0.5 fl oz) fractionated coconut oil or sweet almond oil

1 tbsp (0.5 fl oz) Leucidal® liquid SF (or appropriate amount of another natural preservative)

10 drops essential oil (optional)

## DIRECTIONS

Combine 1 cup water and marshmallow root in a jar. Cover and let it sit for a minimum of 4 hours. Strain with a cheesecloth or fine mesh strainer.

In a medium saucepan, combine remaining 1 cup water and dried herbs, and bring to a boil. Remove from heat and allow the mixture to steep until it has cooled to room temperature. Strain the herbs from the mixture.

Combine the marshmallow infusion and the herb infusion. You'll be using a total of 1 cup of this liquid in the recipe.

Combine coconut oil and essential oil, if using.

Combine 1 cup of the herbal infusion with the vinegar, clay, aloe gel, coconut oil mixture, and Leucidal® liquid SF.

Stir until completely combined, and store in covered jar.

To use, apply to wet hair, starting at the roots and massaging down to the ends of the hair. Let it sit in your hair for 5 minutes, and then rinse.

Once all the product is rinsed from the hair, apply a diluted apple cider vinegar rinse.

CHAPTER ELEVEN

# MASKS

# MASKS

Masks might seem like the ultimate spa-day indulgence, but since most of these recipes use simple kitchen ingredients and come together in moments, you won't actually need much time to seriously treat your skin. Even a weekly 10 minute mask can work wonders!

Some masks brighten, tighten, and tone the skin with drawing or astringent action, while others nourish, boost vitality, plump the skin, and/or temporarily minimize fine lines by adding moisture and nutrients—and you can certainly benefit from using both at different times!

# Rose, Honey & Oat
# MASK

### INGREDIENTS

¼ cup oat flour or finely ground oatmeal

3 tbsp rose (*Rosa* spp.) petal powder

2 tbsp rhassoul clay

2 tbsp (1 fl oz) raw manuka or kanuka honey
(or substitute any raw honey)

2 tbsp (1 fl oz) warm water

### DIRECTIONS

Thoroughly mix finely ground oats, rose powder,
and clay in a small bowl.

Stir honey into the warm water until dissolved, then
gradually mix into dry ingredients until it forms a paste.

Add additional warm water until the mask reaches
desired consistency.

Apply to face, avoiding the eye area. Allow to dry for 15 to
20 minutes, then rinse with warm water. Gently pat skin
dry with a clean towel.

This anti-inflammatory and antimicrobial face mask is a
soothing treat for acne- or rosacea-prone skin, but can be
enjoyed by most skin types. This recipe makes a generous batch,
so feel free to halve if desired.

# Nourishing
# FACIAL MASK

This mask is well-suited for very dry skin in
need of deep moisture and nourishment.

## INGREDIENTS

1½ tsp rhassoul clay

1½ tsp oat flour

1 tbsp (0.5 fl oz) nettle (*Urtica dioica*) leaf infusion

1 tsp avocado oil

## DIRECTIONS

Make nettle infusion using 2 teaspoons nettle and ¼ cup
just-off-the-boil water. Let steep 15 minutes, then strain.

Pour 1 tablespoon nettle infusion into a small bowl.

Stir in clay and oat flour. Let sit for 2–3 minutes
to allow liquid to absorb.

Stir until well-mixed.

Add oil and stir again.

Apply to dry face with fingers or a small brush.

Let sit for 10–20 minutes.

Rinse with warm water. Gently pat skin dry with a clean towel.

Label, store any extra in the refrigerator, and use within 2 days.

# Astringent
# Undereye Mask

Astringent herbs combine with eye-friendly cucumber in
this mask for baggy or puffy eyes.

## INGREDIENTS

2 tsp goldenrod (*Solidago canadensis*) aerial parts
powder and/or lady's mantle (*Alchemilla vulgaris*)
aerial parts powder

1 tsp white cosmetic clay

2–3 tsp cucumber (*Cucumis sativus*) hydrosol

## DIRECTIONS

Combine all dry ingredients.

Slowly add hydrosol until you reach a mud-like
consistency.

Apply gently to the area under the eyes.

Leave on for 20–30 minutes.

Rinse with warm water. Gently pat skin lightly with a
towel to dry.

Follow with undereye serum.

# Clarifying
# FACE MASK

## INGREDIENTS
1 tbsp rhassoul clay

2 tbsp (1 fl oz) lavender (*Lavandula* spp.) hydrosol

1 tsp jojoba or blueberry seed oil

## DIRECTIONS
Pour lavender hydrosol into a small bowl.

Add clay and let sit for 2–3 minutes as the clay absorbs the hydrosol.

Stir until well-mixed.

Add oil and stir again.

Apply to dry face with fingers or a small brush.

Leave in place for 10–20 minutes.

Rinse face with warm water. Gently pat skin dry with a clean towel.

Follow with moisturizer.

Rhassoul clay can help to draw out blackheads, reduce breakouts, and even skin tone. Combined with anti-inflammatory and vulnerary lavender hydrosol and a nourishing oil, this face mask can be used 1-2 times per week to support clear skin.

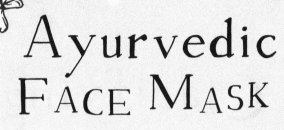

# Ayurvedic Face Mask

### INGREDIENTS

1 tbsp chickpea flour

¼ tsp rose (*Rosa* spp.) petal powder

⅛ tsp turmeric (*Curcuma longa*) rhizome powder

⅛ tsp neem (*Azadirachta indica*) leaf powder

⅛ tsp manjistha (*Rubia cordifolia*) root powder

1–2 tbsp sesame oil (for dry skin) or rose water (for oily skin)

### DIRECTIONS

Combine all dry ingredients.

Slowly add sesame oil or rose water until mixture
reaches a mud-like consistency.

Apply gently to the face.

Leave in place for 15–30 minutes.

Rinse face with warm water. Gently pat skin
lightly with a towel to dry.

Follow with moisturizer.

Chickpea flour, also known as gram or besan flour, is found in many ayurvedic facial formulas as an exfoliant, astringent, and brightener. This recipe combines this age-old ingredient with key ayurvedic herbs for skin health and includes options for both dry and oily skin. If you are familiar with your ayurvedic skin type, *vata-* and *kapha-* type skin benefits from the addition of sesame oil, while *pitta*-type skin does better with rose water. Make a larger batch of the flour and herbal powder portion, if desired, and store for up to 1 year, mixing 3 teaspoons of the mixture with 1-2 tablespoons oil or rose water per use.

# A CLAY MASK
## FOR YOUR SKIN TYPE

Clay is a well-known mask ingredient that detoxifies, tightens, exfoliates, and softens skin. Choose your clay based on your skin type—French green clay or bentonite clay for oily skin, kaolin clay for normal or dry skin. It can be mixed with moisturizing cream for dry skin, water or green tea for oily skin, or chamomile tea or milk for normal skin. As an optional addition, use powdered rose petals for oily skin, or lavender for normal to dry skin.

---

### INGREDIENTS

2 tbsp (1 fl oz) chamomile (*Matricaria chamomilla*) flower tea, green tea (*Camellia sinensis*) leaf tea, water, cream, or milk

1½ tbsp clay of choice

1 tsp raw honey

Rose (*Rosa* spp.) petal or lavender (*Lavandula* spp.) flower bud, powdered (optional)

### DIRECTIONS

In a small bowl, combine clay of choice and liquid of choice, letting the liquid soak the clay, and then stir well. When it has a smooth consistency, add the honey and a few pinches of rose or lavender powder, if using. Feel free to adjust the consistency by adding more liquid or more clay.

Apply mask in a generously thick layer to freshly washed and dried facial skin. Leave on for 10–15 minutes (mask will still be slightly damp).

Rinse face with warm water.
Gently pat skin lightly with a towel to dry.

Follow with moisturizer.

# Seaweed Mask

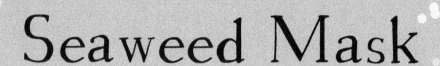

*Adapted from* Herbal Formularies for Health Professionals Vol. 1 *by Jill Stansbury (Stansbury. 2018).*

This seaweed poultice is a simple approach for easing skin inflammation.

## INGREDIENTS

1 tbsp chamomile (*Matricaria chamomilla*) flower

½ cup Irish moss (*Chondrus crispus*) seaweed, dried or 1 tbsp Irish moss seaweed powder

## DIRECTIONS

Place chamomile in a small bowl. Bring 1 cup of water to a boil, and pour boiling water over chamomile. Let steep for 10 minutes, covered.

If using Irish moss powder, add 1 tablespoon powder to ¼ cup chamomile tea and either whisk or use an immersion blender to blend, then let soak for 15 minutes. If using whole seaweed, add ½ cup Irish moss to ½ cup chamomile tea, stir well, and let soak for 15 minutes. Stir occasionally.

Once the Irish moss mixture is gummy, place mask onto face. Keep mask in place for 15–30 minutes.

Rinse face with warm water. Gently pat skin lightly with a towel to dry.

Follow with moisturizer.

# *Exfoliating* HAND MASK

*Adapted from* Organic Body Care Recipes *by Stephanie Tourles*
*(Tourles, 2007).*

This gentle, exfoliating mask is a nice, moisturizing treat for hands, and a good excuse for a hand massage!

## INGREDIENTS

1 tbsp baking soda

1 tsp sunflower seed, grapeseed, sweet almond, olive, or jojoba oil

2 drops essential oil (lavender (*Lavandula* spp.) or sweet orange (*Citrus* x *sinensis*) are nice options)

½ tsp aloe (*Aloe vera*) leaf gel (optional)

## DIRECTIONS

In a small bowl, combine oil and essential oil together and mix well.

Add baking soda and mix well.

Add aloe gel, if using.

Apply to hands, rubbing hands together to spread the mask onto all surfaces of the hands: front, back, in between fingers, and around nails.

Rinse hands with warm water. Gently pat skin lightly with a towel to dry.

Follow with moisturizer.

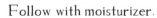

# Clay, Willow, and ZINC MASK

### INGREDIENTS

1 tbsp French green clay
(other types of clay can be used in place of French green clay)

1 tsp willow (*Salix* spp.) bark powder

¼ tsp zinc oxide powder

### DIRECTIONS

Combine the ingredients in a container, and stir
thoroughly to ensure the zinc powder is mixed in well.

Cap until use.

To use, dispense the desired amount: pea sized for a spot
treatment, or about 1-2 teaspoons for a thin mask over the
face or oily portions of the face.

Moisten with just enough water to achieve a smooth consistency.

Apply to clean wet skin, and leave in place
for at least 15 minutes.

Rinse off with warm water. Gently pat skin lightly
with a towel to dry.

Follow with moisturizer.

This could be used as a spot treatment for blemishes or
occasionally as a mask for oily skin prone to redness.
The powder will store indefinitely if you take care to only
moisten the portion you will use at a given time. You may
want to scale the recipe up to make a bigger batch.

# Ayurvedic Pregnant Belly Mask

This recipe is based on a traditional ayurvedic belly paste used to ease the itchy skin that is so common in pregnancy as well as to minimize stretch marks. Some of the herbs in the traditional formula have sustainability issues or are difficult to find, and have been replaced with more common herbs.

## INGREDIENTS

1 tbsp licorice (*Glycyrrhiza glabra*) root powder

1 tbsp manjistha (*Rubia cordifolia*) root powder

1 tbsp triphala (*Terminalia bellirica*, *T. chebula*, and *Phyllanthus emblica*) fruit powder

1 tbsp gotu kola (*Centella asiatica*) leaf powder

1 tbsp rose (*Rosa* spp.) petal powder

1 tsp nutmeg (*Myristica fragrans*) seed powder

## DIRECTIONS

Combine powders in a glass jar. Label, and store in a cool, dark place for up to 12 months.

Combine 2 teaspoons herbal powder with enough milk or water to make a smooth paste.

Apply to belly and chest approximately 20 minutes before showering/bathing.

Rinse in shower/bath.

After shower/bath, apply moisturizer.

# ⇝ Green Tea ⇜
## FACIAL MASK

Matcha green tea makes a beautiful green mask that astringes and tones skin while aloe gel and honey lend some soothing moisture.

### INGREDIENTS

2 tbsp matcha or other green tea (*Camellia sinensis*) leaf powder

4 tsp aloe (*Aloe vera*) leaf gel

1–2 tsp raw honey

### DIRECTIONS

Combine all ingredients and mix well. Adjust proportions as needed to get the consistency you like: add more honey and/or tea powder if it's too drippy, or thin with more aloe.

Apply gently to the face, avoiding the eyes.

Leave in place for 20–40 minutes.

Rinse face with warm water. Gently pat skin lightly with a towel to dry.

Follow with moisturizer.

# Turmeric, Honey, and Yogurt
## FACE MASK

*Adapted from Kate Kordsmeier (Kordsmeier. 2017).*

You've probably heard about turmeric's anti-inflammatory properties when taken internally, but it is also traditionally used to calm inflammation of the skin, and it also acts as an astringent vulnerary. Honey's antimicrobial power and the probiotics provided by yogurt make this an excellent choice for acne-prone skin.

### INGREDIENTS

1 tbsp plain yogurt

1 tsp turmeric (*Curcuma longa*) rhizome powder

1 tsp raw honey

### DIRECTIONS

In a small bowl, combine yogurt, turmeric powder, and honey. Mix well.

After washing face, apply mask. Let sit for approximately 15 minutes.

Rinse face with warm water. Gently pat skin dry with a clean towel.

# Lemon Balm
## SHEET MASK

This recipe can easily be adapted for your skin's needs.
Substitute any hydrosol in place of the lemon balm!

### INGREDIENTS

¼ cup (2 fl oz) lemon balm (*Melissa officinalis*) hydrosol

1 tsp raw honey, aloe (*Aloe vera*) leaf juice, or milk of choice

1 tsp serum of choice

### DIRECTIONS

Create your sheet mask template: Cut a circle the size of
your face from a clean cotton hand towel or washcloth and cut
out holes for your eyes, nose, and mouth. (Alternatively,
use strips of rice paper or nori seaweed!)

Combine all ingredients together in a shallow bowl
or storage container.

Soak mask in bowl/container until it is fully saturated.

Remove mask and gently squeeze until mask stops dripping,
but is still saturated with fluid.

Place mask over face and leave in place for 15–40 minutes.

Gently peel away the mask and rinse the face with warm
water. Gently pat skin lightly with a towel to dry.

Follow with moisturizer.

To reuse your mask cloth, wash on gentle, or
hand wash and hang to dry.

# HONEY
## AND WINE MASK

*Adapted from 100 Organic Skincare Recipes by Jessica Ress (Ress. 2014).*

This straight-from-the-kitchen-cabinet facial mask is chock full of antioxidants, combining emollient chia seeds with astringent red wine and our favorite skin care pantry item: honey!

### INGREDIENTS

1 tsp raw honey

1½ tsp red wine

½ tsp ground chia seed

### DIRECTIONS

Combine the honey and wine in a small bowl.

Stir in the ground chia seeds and mix well to combine. Adjust the consistency by adding a bit more honey or chia seeds if needed.

Spread a thin layer on the skin, avoiding the eyes, and leave in place for at least 15 minutes.

Rinse face with warm water. Gently pat skin lightly with a towel to dry.

Follow with moisturizer.

*The beauty of homemade skin care is that so many things can be created from simple ingredients that are already at home in your kitchen!*

BOTANICAL SKIN CARE COURSE

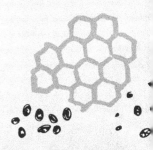

# CHAPTER TWELVE

# OILS

# OILS

Infused herbal oils are a key ingredient in many homemade skin products. Herbs add a wealth of skin-supporting properties to the nutritive and moisturizing effects of oils and allow you to customize your recipes to suit specific skin types and conditions. But herbal oils aren't only an ingredient, they can also be used on their own to help keep your skin and your whole body happy.

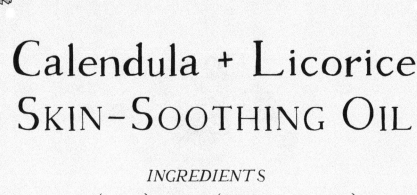

# Calendula + Licorice Skin-Soothing Oil

### INGREDIENTS

¾ cup (6 fl oz) calendula (*Calendula officinalis*)
flower-infused grapeseed oil

¼ cup (2 fl oz) licorice (*Glycyrrhiza glabra*)
root-infused jojoba oil

20 drops helichrysum (*Helichrysum italicum*) essential oil

½ tsp vitamin E oil

### DIRECTIONS

Make the infused oils using the instructions in the
herb-infused oil tutorial.

Combine infused oils and add remaining ingredients. Mix well.

For ease of use, transfer a portion of the oil to a small
glass dropper bottle and label.

Prior to use, mix ingredients in small glass dropper bottle
by gently rolling the bottle in warm hands.

Apply a thin layer to itchy, irritated skin.

Store in a cool, dry place for up to 1 year.

This simple combination of infused oils is ideal for soothing
any kind of dry, itchy, or irritated skin, and can be particularly
helpful for soothing the relentless itch of contact dermatitis.
Apply to troublesome spots, or smooth all over for
extremely dry or inflamed skin.

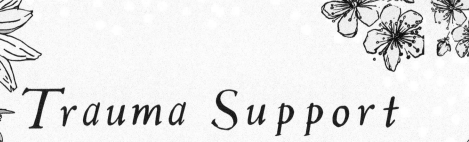

# Trauma Support
# OIL

*Adapted from* Therapeutic Herb Manual *by Ed Smith*
*(Smith. 2008).*

### INGREDIENTS

¼ cup (2 fl oz) oil infused with arnica
(*Arnica* spp.) flower

⅛ cup (1 fl oz) oil infused with calendula
(*Calendula officinalis*) flower

⅛ cup (1 fl oz) oil infused with St. John's wort
(*Hypericum perforatum*) aerial parts

### DIRECTIONS

Make infused oils using the instructions in the
herb-infused oil tutorial.

Combine oils in a 4-ounce glass bottle and shake well.

Label, and store in a cool, dark place for up to 1 year.

To use, massage gently onto affected area.

This oil is a useful adjunct while healing from physical
trauma, such as strains, sprains, fractures, bruises, and
before and after surgery.

# Calendula + Friends
## INFUSED OIL

This nourishing infused oil works wonders for eczema and other dry, itchy, and irritated skin conditions, and is safe for baby and adult skin alike. If smoothing on an herbal oil is too messy for your taste, transform the oil into a salve by following the Calendula and Friends Salve recipe.

### INGREDIENTS
1 cup (8 fl oz) sesame oil

¼ cup calendula (*Calendula officinalis*) flower

⅛ cup licorice (*Glycyrrhiza glabra*) root

⅛ cup plantain (*Plantago* spp.) leaf

### DIRECTIONS
Grind dried herbs in a mortar and pestle or break them up in your clean hands to produce smaller pieces.

Fill a dry, heat-safe glass quart jar with herbs.

Pour oil over herbs, making sure herbs are completely covered and oil is at least 1 inch above the top of the herbs. Use a clean, dry spoon or chopstick to mix thoroughly so all surfaces of the herbs are coated and no air bubbles remain.

Place a square piece of natural waxed paper on top of the jar, then seal the jar with a lid (this protects oil from any chemical coating that may be on the lid).

Roll jar back and forth in your hands to continue to thoroughly mix the herb and oil, focusing your intention for the infused oil.

Place the jar in a saucepan or slow cooker that has been filled with 2–3 inches of water and place a few jar lids under the jar to protect the base. Heat on very low heat for 4–8 hours (or more), making sure oil does not get warmer than 120–140 degrees F. (Alternatively, use a double boiler.) Remove jar from saucepan and allow to cool.

Place a cheesecloth-lined strainer inside a large bowl with a spout. Pour the contents from the jar into the strainer. With clean dry hands, gather the ends of the cheesecloth together and squeeze the remaining oil from the herb into the bowl. You'll want to squeeze hard to get every last drop!

Pour the oil into a clean glass jar, cap, and let it settle overnight or for a few days.

Strain the oil again, being careful to avoid pouring out any of the remaining herb particulates that have settled to the bottom of the jar.

Pour the oil into clean and dry glass bottle(s) or jar(s) (ideally dark-colored glass bottles/jars to protect from light). Cap tightly.

Label jar(s) and store in a cool, dark place for up to 1 year.

# Calendula Cuticle OIL

*Adapted from* Plant-Powered Beauty *by Amy Galper and Christina Daigneault (Galper & Daigneault. 2018).*

Treat yourself to a manicure or pedicure in the comfort of your own home: draw up an herbal hand/foot bath, follow with a hand/foot scrub, and apply calendula cuticle oil before applying polish (or not!); this cuticle oil is also well-suited to daily use.

## INGREDIENTS

¼ cup (2 fl oz) sesame oil

2 tbsp (1 fl oz) castor oil

2 tbsp (1 fl oz) olive oil

¼ cup calendula
(*Calendula officinalis*)
flower

## DIRECTIONS

Grind calendula in a mortar and pestle or break it up in your clean hands to produce smaller pieces.

Fill a dry, heat-safe glass half-pint jar with herbs.

Combine oils and pour over calendula, making sure calendula is completely covered and oil is at least 1 inch above the top of the calendula. Use a clean, dry spoon or chopstick to mix thoroughly so all surfaces of the herbs are coated and no air bubbles remain.

Place a square piece of natural waxed paper on top of the jar, then seal jar with a lid (this protects oil from any chemical coating that may be on the lid).

Roll jar back and forth in your hands to continue to thoroughly mix the herb and oil, focusing your intention for the infused oil.

Place the jar in a saucepan or slow cooker that has been filled with 2-3 inches of water and place a few jar lids under the jar to protect the base. Heat on very low heat for 4-8 hours (or more), making sure oil does not get warmer than 120-140 degrees F. (Alternatively, use a double boiler.) Remove jar from saucepan and allow to cool.

Place a cheesecloth-lined strainer inside a large bowl with a spout. Pour the contents from the jar into the strainer. With clean dry hands, gather the ends of the cheesecloth together and squeeze the remaining oil from the herb into the bowl. You'll want to squeeze hard to get every last drop!

Pour the oil into a clean glass jar, cap, and let it settle overnight or for a few days.

Strain the oil again, being careful to avoid pouring out any of the remaining herb particulates that have settled to the bottom of the jar.

Pour the oil into clean and dry glass bottle(s) or jar(s) (ideally dark-colored glass bottles/jars to protect from light). Cap tightly.

Label jar(s) and store in a cool, dark place for up to 1 year.

Apply 1-2 drops of cuticle oil to each cuticle and massage.

# Vatta-Pitta Abhyanga Oil

*Adapted from Brenda Igler (Igler, 2016).*

Note that the following recipe provides instructions on the traditional way to make an ayurvedic oil, but the recipe can also be made using a standard oil infusion.

## INGREDIENTS

1 tsp licorice (*Glycyrrhiza glabra*) root

1 tsp valerian (*Valeriana officinalis*) root

1½ tsp ginger (*Zingiber officinale*) rhizome

2 tbsp bala (*Sida cordifolia*) root powder

1 tsp amalaki (*Phyllanthus emblica*) fruit powder

1½ tsp guduchi (*Tinospora cordifolia*) stem powder

1 tsp manjistha (*Rubia cordifolia*) root powder

1½ tsp St. John's wort (*Hypericum perforatum*) aerial parts

½ cup (4 fl oz) sesame oil

2 cups (16 fl oz) water

## DIRECTIONS

In a medium-sized pot, bring the water to boil and add the licorice, valerian, and ginger. Turn down to a simmer and cook until the water is reduced by 50%.

Remove from heat and add the bala, amalaki, guduchi, manjistha and St. John's wort. Cover and let steep for 30 minutes.

Add the sesame oil, put on a very low simmer, and stir occasionally until all of the water has cooked off. These are some ways to determine when all of the water has evaporated and you only have pure herbal oil left:

-The bubbles in the mixture become smaller (oil creates smaller bubbles than water).

-Oil becomes clear as the water evaporates. You may be able to see through to the bottom of the pot more clearly.

-Hold a dry glass over your pot. This will help detect condensation if water is still present.

-Finally, when you strain the mixture, you should end up with 4 fluid ounces of oil (the original amount you put in).

Strain through several layers of cheesecloth. Label, store in a glass bottle for up to 1 year, and enjoy as a lovely skin oil!

# Nourishing
## HAND OIL

*Adapted from* Grow Your Own Drugs *by* James Wong *(Wong. 2009).*

Rich oils and sweetly scented essential oils are a feast for the overworked skin on hands. Bonus: this hand oil is super easy to make!

### INGREDIENTS

4 tbsp (2 fl oz) avocado oil

2 tbsp (1 fl oz) evening primrose oil

2 tsp vitamin E oil

9 drops sandalwood (*Santalum album*)
essential oil, sustainably sourced

9 drops lemon
(*Citrus* x *limon*)
essential oil

9 drops geranium (*Pelargonium* spp.)
essential oil

### DIRECTIONS

Combine oils in a glass measuring cup.

Transfer to a 2-ounce dropper bottle
or a roller ball applicator.

Massage into hands as needed.

Store in a cool, dark place for
up to 6 months.

# Crampy Belly Oil

Antispasmodic herbs are infused in deeply-penetrating oils in this herbal preparation ideal for menstrual or gastrointestinal cramping. For extra support, after applying the oil, cover the area with flannel and a hot water bottle, lie back, and relax!

## INGREDIENTS

½ cup (4 fl oz) castor oil

½ cup (4 fl oz) sweet almond oil

2 tbsp ginger (*Zingiber officinale*) rhizome

2 tbsp cramp bark (*Viburnum opulus*) bark

1 tbsp mugwort (*Artemisia vulgaris*) aerial parts

1 tbsp chamomile (*Matricaria chamomilla*) flower

20-75 drops lavender (*Lavandula* spp.) essential oil (optional)

## DIRECTIONS

Grind herbs in a mortar and pestle or break them up in your clean hands to produce smaller pieces.

Fill a dry, heat-safe glass quart jar with herbs.

Combine oils and pour over herbs, making sure herbs are completely covered and oil is at least 1 inch above the top of the herbs. Use a clean, dry spoon or chopstick to mix thoroughly so all surfaces of the herbs are coated and no air bubbles remain.

Place a square piece of natural waxed paper on top of the jar, then seal jar with a lid (this protects oil from any chemical coating that may be on the lid).

Roll jar back and forth in your hands to continue to thoroughly mix the herb and oil, focusing your intention for the infused oil.

Place the jar in a saucepan or slow cooker that has been filled with 2-3 inches of water and place a few jar lids under the jar to protect the base. Heat on very low heat for 4-8 hours (or more), making sure oil does not get warmer than 120-140 degrees F. (Alternatively, use a double boiler.) Remove jar from saucepan and allow to cool.

Place a cheesecloth-lined strainer inside a large bowl with a spout. Pour the contents from the jar into the strainer. With clean dry hands, gather the ends of the cheesecloth together and squeeze the remaining oil from the herb into the bowl. You'll want to squeeze hard to get every last drop!

Pour the oil into a clean glass jar, cap, and let it settle overnight or for a few days.

Strain the oil again, being careful to avoid pouring out any of the remaining herb particulates that have settled to the bottom of the jar.

Pour the oil into clean and dry glass bottle(s) or jar(s) (ideally dark-colored glass bottles/jars to protect from light), and add essential oils if desired. Cap tightly.

Label jar(s) and store in a cool, dark place for up to 1 year.

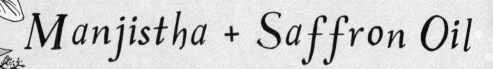

# Manjistha + Saffron Oil

According to Ayurveda, manjistha has a special herbal action known as *varnya* (improves complexion) (Pole, 2006), and is often used, along with saffron, in topical preparations aimed at evening out skin tone.

## INGREDIENTS

½ cup (4 fl oz) sesame oil or papaya seed oil

¼ cup manjistha (*Rubia cordifolia*) root powder

1 tbsp saffron (*Crocus sativus*) thread

## DIRECTIONS

Fill a dry, heat-safe half-pint glass jar with herbs.

Pour oil over herbs, making sure herbs are completely covered and oil is at least 1 inch above the top of the herbs. Use a clean, dry spoon or chopstick to mix thoroughly so all surfaces of the herbs are coated and no air bubbles remain.

Place a square piece of natural waxed paper on top of the jar, then seal jar with a lid (this protects oil from any chemical coating that may be on the lid).

Roll jar back and forth in your hands to continue to thoroughly mix the herb and oil, focusing your intention for the infused oil.

Place the jar in a saucepan or slow cooker that has been filled with 2–3 inches of water and place a few jar lids under the jar to protect the base. Heat on very low heat for 4–8 hours (or more), making sure oil does not get warmer than 120–140 degrees F. (Alternatively, use a double boiler.) Remove jar from saucepan and allow to cool.

Place a cheesecloth-lined strainer inside a large bowl with a spout. Pour the contents from the jar into the strainer. With clean, dry hands, gather the ends of the cheesecloth together and squeeze the remaining oil from the herb into the bowl. You'll want to squeeze hard to get every last drop!

Pour the oil into a clean glass jar, cap, and let it settle overnight or for a few days.

Strain the oil again, being careful to avoid pouring out any of the remaining herb particulates that have settled to the bottom of the jar.

Pour the oil into clean and dry glass bottle(s) or jar(s) (ideally dark-colored glass bottles/jars to protect from light). Cap tightly.

Label, and store in a cool, dark place for up to 1 year.

# BABY
# MASSAGE
# OIL

Baby massage is such a relaxing way to bond with and nurture your little one. Why not add some gentle herbal friends to the massage oil? Calendula can help to soothe the sensitive skin of baby, while the smell of lavender and chamomile may just relax both of you even more! Not just for babies, children and adults can benefit from this massage oil as well!

## INGREDIENTS

1½ cups (12 fl oz) sunflower oil

¼ cup chamomile (*Matricaria chamomilla*) flower

¼ cup calendula (*Calendula officinalis*) flower

⅛ cup lavender (*Lavandula* spp.) flower bud

## DIRECTIONS

Grind dried herbs in a mortar and pestle or break them up in your clean hands to produce smaller pieces.

Fill a dry, heat-safe glass quart jar with herbs.

Pour oil over herbs, making sure herbs are completely covered and oil is at least 1 inch above the top of the herbs. Use a clean, dry spoon or chopstick to mix thoroughly so all surfaces of the herbs are coated and no air bubbles remain.

Place a square piece of natural waxed paper on top of the jar, then seal the jar with a lid (this protects oil from any chemical coating that may be on the lid).

Roll jar back and forth in your hands to continue to thoroughly mix the herb and oil, focusing your intention for the infused oil.

Place the jar in a saucepan or slow cooker that has been filled with 2–3 inches of water and place a few jar lids under the jar to protect the base. Heat on very low heat for 4–8 hours (or more), making sure oil does not get warmer than 120–140 degrees F. (Alternatively, use a double boiler.) Remove jar from saucepan and allow to cool.

Place a cheesecloth-lined strainer inside a large bowl with a spout. Pour the contents from the jar into the strainer. With clean dry hands, gather the ends of the cheesecloth together and squeeze the remaining oil from the herb into the bowl. You'll want to squeeze hard to get every last drop!

Pour the oil into a clean glass jar, cap, and let it settle overnight or for a few days.

Strain the oil again, being careful to avoid pouring out any of the remaining herb particulates that have settled to the bottom of the jar.

Pour the oil into clean and dry glass bottle(s) or jar(s) (ideally dark-colored glass bottles/jars to protect from light). Cap tightly.

Label jar(s) and store in a cool, dark place for up to 1 year.

# Balsam Poplar
# BUD-INFUSED OIL

## INGREDIENTS

Balsam poplar
(*Populus balsamifera*
or *P. angustifolia*)
or
black cottonwood
(*P. trichocarpa*)
leaf bud (fresh;
harvested in spring)

Olive or moringa oil
(enough to cover buds)

---

The analgesic and
anti-inflammatory
properties of
balsam poplar
buds make them a
soothing addition
to preparations
for psoriasis and
other irritating skin
conditions. Turn
this oil into a salve
(see Balm of Gilead
recipe), or simply rub
the oil onto affected
areas of the skin.

## DIRECTIONS

Fill a dry, sterilized heat-safe glass jar
approximately ¾ full with buds.

Pour oil over buds, making sure buds are
completely covered and oil is at least 1 inch above
the top of the herbs. Use a clean, dry spoon or
chopstick to mix thoroughly so all surfaces of the
buds are coated and no air bubbles remain.

Place a square piece of natural waxed paper on top
of the jar, then seal the jar with a lid (this protects oil
from any chemical coating that may be on the lid).

Roll jar back and forth in your hands to continue
to thoroughly mix the herb and oil, focusing your
intention for the infused oil.

Place the jar in a saucepan or slow cooker that
has been filled with 2-3 inches of water and place
a few jar lids under the jar to protect the base.
Heat on very low heat for 4-8 hours (or more),
making sure oil does not get warmer than 120-140
degrees F. (Alternatively, use a double boiler.)
Remove jar from saucepan and allow to cool.

Place a cheesecloth-lined strainer inside a large
bowl with a spout. Pour the contents from the jar
into the strainer. With clean, dry hands, gather the
ends of the cheesecloth together and squeeze the
remaining oil from the herb into the bowl. You'll
want to squeeze hard to get every last drop!

Pour the oil into clean and dry sterilized glass
bottles or jars (ideally dark-colored glass jars to
protect from light). Cap tightly.

Label jar(s) and store in a cool, dark place
for up to 1 year.

*Many of us take a close look at ingredients when we are purchasing food for the dinner table, but might not take ingredients into consideration when shopping for cosmetics, shampoo, soap, and other personal care items. However, the average commercial skin care product contains a handful (or more!) of harmful chemicals, and because these substances may be absorbed through the skin, we might not want to put anything on our skin that we wouldn't also eat.*

BOTANICAL SKIN CARE COURSE

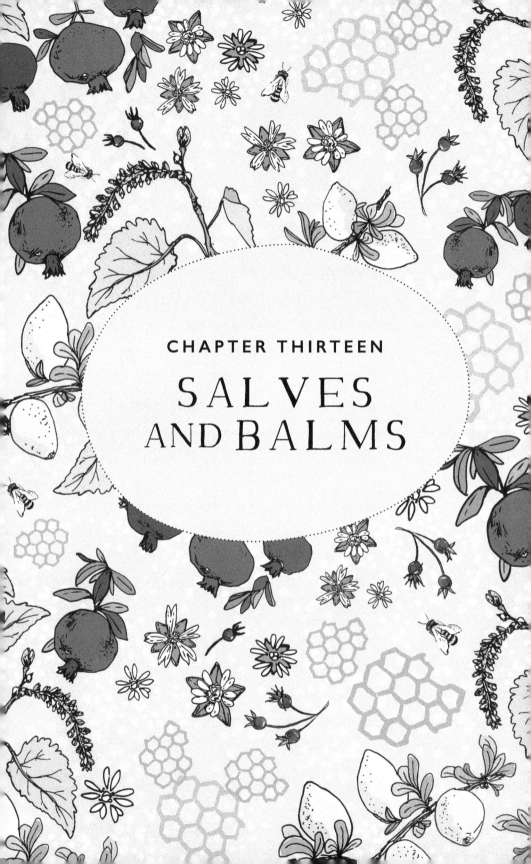

# CHAPTER THIRTEEN

# SALVES AND BALMS

# SALVES AND BALMS

Salves and balms are great ways to use herbal oils—they travel well, can be easily applied, and offer an emollient base that protects and nourishes the skin. Many of these salves are multipurpose and can be used for a whole host of skin issues from simple dry skin and chapped lips to bumps, scrapes, and bruises. You can also create customized balms for support in specific situations like fungal infections or viral outbreaks—once you know how to make your own salves, the possibilities are endless.

# LIP BALM

This general recipe can be adapted to include your
favorite herb-infused oil (calendula (*Calendula officinalis*) flower,
black birch (*Betula lenta*) or yellow birch (*B. allegheniensis*) bark,
peppermint (*Mentha x piperita*) leaf, and vanilla (*Vanilla planifolia*)
bean are favorites) or preferred essential oils
(lemon balm (*Melissa officinalis*), peppermint (*Mentha x piperita*),
or sweet orange (*Citrus x sinensis*) are nice).
Base oils can include olive, sweet almond, jojoba, sunflower,
coconut, and/or grapeseed, to name just a few. A bit of castor oil
adds a shiny gloss, and a teaspoon of honey a sweet touch.

## INGREDIENTS

3-4 tbsp (1.5-2 fl oz)
plain or herb-infused oil

1 tbsp beeswax

1 tbsp shea butter

10 drops essential oil of
choice

## DIRECTIONS

Combine oil, beeswax, and shea butter in a
double boiler over low heat (or a glass or
ceramic bowl or canning jar over a small
saucepan of simmering water), stirring
occasionally until completely melted.

Dip a clean spoon into the formula and
place it into a refrigerator so the salve
will cool quickly and you can determine if
its consistency is what you desire. If the
sample is too soft, add a little more wax to
the warm salve; if the sample is too hard,
add a little more of the infused oil.

Stir in essential oils.

Pour into tins or lip balm tubes and let cool.

Cap and store in a cool, dark place
for up to 1 year.

# Balm *of* Gilead

## INGREDIENTS

1 cup (8 fl oz) balsam poplar bud-infused oil
(see previous recipe)

2-4 tbsp beeswax

## DIRECTIONS

Place oil in a saucepan over low heat.

Add beeswax to the warmed oil. Continue to heat the mixture (over low heat), stirring with a sterilized spoon until the beeswax has melted.

Dip a sterilized spoon into the mixture and place it into a refrigerator so the salve will cool quickly and you can determine if its consistency is what you desire. If the sample is too soft, add a little more wax to the warm salve; if the sample is too hard, add a little more of the infused oil.

While warm, pour individual portions into appropriate containers and allow to cool at room temperature.

Once cool, put the lids on and label. Store in a cool, dark place for up to 1 year.

This salve made with balsam poplar is popularly known as balm of Gilead—a soothing balm for everything from psoriasis to arthritis.

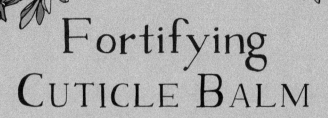

# Fortifying
# Cuticle Balm

*Adapted from* Natural Beauty: 200 Tips, Techniques, and Recipes
for Natural Beauty *by Shannon Buck (Buck, 2014).*

## INGREDIENTS

1½ tbsp shea butter

1½ tbsp beeswax

1 tbsp (0.5 fl oz)
pomegranate seed oil or
rosehip seed oil

1 tbsp (0.5 fl oz)
argan oil

¼ tsp vitamin E oil

3-5 drops rose (*Rosa*
spp.) otto or $CO_2$
extract

This nourishing balm
can be used as part of
a weekly hand or foot
treatment or massaged
in nightly before bed to
help keep the cuticles
soft and supple and
prevent tears and
breakage.

## DIRECTIONS

Combine shea butter and beeswax in a
double boiler over low heat (or a glass
or ceramic bowl or canning jar over a
small saucepan of simmering water) until
shea butter and beeswax have melted and
ingredients are thoroughly combined.

Stir in pomegranate seed oil and argan oil.

Dip a clean spoon into the formula and
place it into a refrigerator so the salve will
cool quickly and you can determine if its
consistency is what you desire. If the sample
is too soft, add a little more wax to the
warm salve; if the sample is too hard, add a
little more of the infused oil.

Add vitamin E oil and rose otto or extract.

Transfer to a small jar for storage and
allow to cool.

Store in a cool, dark place for up
to 6 months.

Massage into cuticles and nails during
manicure or as a daily treatment.

# Rescue Balm
## *for* DRY HANDS

*Adapted from* Healing Herbal Infusions *by Colleen Codekas (Codekas, 2018).*

**Hard-working hands need a hard-working herbal balm!**

## INGREDIENTS

¼ cup lavender (*Lavandula* spp.) flower bud

2 tbsp violet (*Viola* spp.) aerial parts or plantain (*Plantago* spp.) leaf

2 tbsp comfrey (*Symphytum officinale*) leaf or chickweed (*Stellaria media*) aboveground parts

¼ cup (2 fl oz) olive oil

¼ cup (2 fl oz) sweet almond oil

¼ cup (2 fl oz) avocado oil

1 tbsp (0.5 fl oz) castor oil

2 tbsp beeswax

2½ tbsp shea butter

20 drops total lavender (*Lavandula* spp.), sustainably sourced frankincense (*Boswellia* spp.), and/or geranium (*Pelargonium* spp.) essential oil

## DIRECTIONS

In a clean, dry glass pint jar, combine lavender, chickweed, violet (or plantain), and comfrey (or chickweed). Over this, pour the olive, sweet almond, avocado, and castor oils. Stir to combine, making sure that herbs are completely covered with oil. Add a bit more oil, if needed. Complete preparation of the herb-infused oil using the instructions in the herb-infused oil tutorial.

Combine ½ cup herb-infused oil, beeswax, and shea butter in a double boiler over low heat (or a glass or ceramic bowl or canning jar over a small saucepan of simmering water), stirring occasionally until completely melted.

Dip a clean spoon into the formula and place it into a refrigerator so the salve will cool quickly and you can determine if its consistency is what you desire. If the sample is too soft, add a little more wax to the warm salve; if the sample is too hard, add a little more of the infused oil.

Stir in essential oils.

Pour into tins or jars and let cool.

Label, cap, and store in a cool, dark place for up to 1 year.

# Black Walnut
## *Antifungal Salve*

This recipe can be made using mostly temperate climate ingredients (and the common ingredient olive oil) or with the fabulous addition of tea tree oil. Apply to affected areas, such as feet and toenails. This salve may stain skin and/or clothing!

### INGREDIENTS

1 cup (8 fl oz) olive oil

½ cup black walnut (*Juglans nigra*) hull (the green outer shell, preferably fresh)

2 tbsp beeswax

10 drops tea tree (*Melaleuca alternifolia*) essential oil (optional)

### DIRECTIONS

Make black walnut–infused oil using the instructions in the herb–infused oil tutorial.

Combine herb–infused oil and beeswax in a double boiler over low heat (or a glass or ceramic bowl or canning jar over a small saucepan of simmering water), stirring occasionally until completely melted.

Dip a clean spoon into the formula and place it into a refrigerator so the salve will cool quickly and you can determine if its consistency is what you desire. If the sample is too soft, add a little more wax to the warm salve; if the sample is too hard, add a little more of the infused oil.

Stir in essential oil if desired.

Pour into tins or jars and let cool.

Label, cap, and store in a cool, dark place for up to 1 year.

# Clearing Chest Rub

Topical preparations aren't just for skin support! This volatile oil-rich balm can help to clear the congestion of respiratory viruses and allergies.

## INGREDIENTS

½ cup (4 fl oz) sesame or sweet almond oil

½ tsp menthol crystals

1 tbsp beeswax

20–30 drops balsam fir (*Abies balsamea*), camphor (*Cinnamomum camphora*), or eucalyptus (*Eucalyptus* spp.) essential oil (Note: for children 2–6, do not use eucalyptus essential oil; this recipe is not recommended for children under 2.)

## DIRECTIONS

Place oil in a double boiler over low heat (or glass bowl over a saucepan of simmering water).

Add wax to the warmed oil. Continue to heat the mixture (over low heat), stirring with a clean spoon until the beeswax has melted.

Dip a clean spoon into the formula and place it into a refrigerator so the salve will cool quickly and you can determine if its consistency is what you desire. If the sample is too soft, add a little more wax to the warm salve; if the sample is too hard, add a little more of the infused oil.

Add menthol crystals and essential oil. Stir until crystals are dissolved.

Pour individual portions into appropriate containers and allow to cool at room temperature.

Once cool, put the lids on and label.

Store in a cool, dark place for up to 1 year.

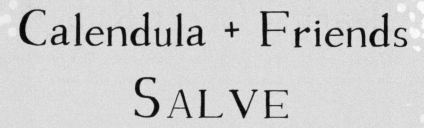

# Calendula + Friends
# SALVE

Turn Calendula and Friends Herbal Oil into a salve for easy application on eczema-prone, dry, itchy, or irritated skin.

## INGREDIENTS

1 cup (8 fl oz) calendula and friends herbal oil
(see Calendula and Friends Oil recipe)

2–4 tbsp beeswax

## DIRECTIONS

Place infused oil and beeswax in a double boiler over low heat (or a glass or ceramic bowl or canning jar over a small saucepan of simmering water) until beeswax has melted and ingredients are thoroughly combined.

Dip a clean spoon into the formula and place it into a refrigerator so the salve will cool quickly and you can determine if its consistency is what you desire. If the sample is too soft, add a little more wax to the warm salve; if the sample is too hard, add a little more of the infused oil.

While warm, pour individual portions into appropriate containers and allow to cool at room temperature.

Once cool, put the lids on and label.

Store in a cool, dark place for up to 1 year.

# Propolis Salve

## INGREDIENTS

¼ tsp propolis tincture

1½ tsp beeswax

2½ tbsp (1.25 fl oz) apricot kernel, grapeseed, or olive oil
infused with chamomile (*Matricaria chamomilla*) flower
(or plain oil)

## DIRECTIONS

Combine beeswax and oil in a double boiler (or a glass
or ceramic bowl or canning jar over a small saucepan
of simmering water). Heat over a gentle simmer until
beeswax is melted.

Remove from heat and stir in propolis tincture.

Pour into a 2-ounce tin or glass jar; allow to cool
completely before capping.

Label, and store in a cool, dark place for up to 1 year.

Propolis adds an incredible antimicrobial boost to any skin
salve; in this recipe, it's combined with chamomile to make a
restorative, vulnerary balm that can be used to help skin heal
up quickly and reduce the chance of infection. Do make sure to
practice excellent hygiene if you're using any salve on cuts or
abraded skin; always apply using a clean spoon, cotton swab, or
other tool—no fingers in the salve jar!

# Cold Sore Salve

Lemon balm essential oil can be particularly helpful for cold sores, but it is frightfully expensive; feel free to leave it out, and you'll still have an excellent salve to help soothe and even stave off outbreaks.

## INGREDIENTS

2 tbsp (1 fl oz) olive oil

2 tbsp (1 fl oz) coconut oil

4 tsp lemon balm (*Melissa officinalis*) aerial parts

4 tsp St. John's wort (*Hypericum perforatum*) aerial parts

4 tsp hyssop (*Hyssopus officinalis*) aerial parts

½–1 tbsp beeswax

20 drops lemon balm (*Melissa officinalis*) essential oil (optional)

5 drops tea tree (*Melaleuca alternifolia*) essential oil (optional)

## DIRECTIONS

Make a lemon balm-, hyssop-, and St. John's wort-infused oil using the instructions in the herb-infused oil tutorial. Note that ¼ cup is the amount of finished herbal oil to include in the recipe—you may need to start with more oil when making the herb-infused oil, as the herbs will soak up some of the oil (if you forget to do this, just top off with some plain oil as needed for this recipe).

Once the oil is complete and herbs have been strained out, gently melt the beeswax and oils together in a double boiler (or a glass or ceramic bowl or canning jar over a small saucepan of simmering water).

Remove from heat and add essential oils, if using.

Pour into small jars or tins; allow to cool completely before capping.

Label, and store in a cool, dark place for up to 1 year.

Apply to lips and surrounding skin daily or as needed.

# Pine Resin Salve

The antimicrobial and drawing properties of evergreen resins such as pine, fir, and spruce can be supportive for skin wounds and splinters. Substitute oils infused with plantain, calendula, comfrey, and/or yarrow for the plain oil in order to incorporate more vulnerary and antimicrobial herbs to support the body's wound-healing process. Be sure to harvest only excess resin that has dripped below a wound in the tree bark, as the resin is the tree's own wound-healing mechanism. Note that pine resin is easier to work with (less sticky) if stored in the freezer; it can then be placed into a thick plastic bag and smashed into granules with a hammer for easier measurement.

## INGREDIENTS

¼ cup pine (*Pinus* spp.) resin

½ cup (4 fl oz) almond, grapeseed, or olive oil

1–2 tbsp beeswax

## DIRECTIONS

Place the pine resin and oil in a double boiler (or a glass or ceramic bowl or canning jar over a small saucepan of simmering water). Bring water to a gentle simmer and heat until resin has melted and combined with oil.

Strain mixture through a coffee filter or fine mesh strainer (since resin can be hard to wash off, don't use your best strainer!).

Return to double boiler and add beeswax. Gently heat until mixture is melted.

Dip a clean spoon into the formula and place it into a refrigerator so the salve will cool quickly and you can determine if its consistency is what you desire. If the sample is too soft, add a little more wax to the warm salve; if the sample is too hard, add a little more of the oil.

Pour into tins or jars and let cool, then cap.

Label, and store in a cool, dark place for up to 1 year.

# Baby Bum
## BALM

This cloth-diaper-friendly diaper rash preparation contains anti-inflammatory and vulnerary calendula, along with calcium-rich marshmallow, which can help to stimulate new tissue growth (Hoffmann, 2003). Oat flour thickens up the balm and provides proteins that may help to preserve barrier integrity. Be sure to use a clean finger or utensil when retrieving the balm from the jar to apply to baby's bottom!

## INGREDIENTS

¼ cup (2 fl oz) coconut oil infused with calendula (*Calendula officinalis*) flower and marshmallow (*Althaea officinalis*) root

3 tbsp shea butter

2 tsp beeswax

2 tbsp oat flour

## DIRECTIONS

Make calendula- and marshmallow-infused coconut oil using the instructions in the herb-infused oil tutorial. Note that ¼ cup is the amount of finished herbal oil to include in the recipe—you may need to start with more oil when making the herb-infused oil, as the herbs will soak up some of the oil (if you forget to do this, just top off with some plain oil as needed for this recipe).

Place coconut oil, shea butter, and beeswax in a double boiler over low heat (or glass bowl over a saucepan of simmering water) until shea butter and beeswax have melted and ingredients are thoroughly combined.

Dip a clean spoon into the formula and place it into a refrigerator so the salve will cool quickly and you can determine if its consistency is what you desire. If the sample is too soft, add a little more wax to the warm salve; if the sample is too hard, add a little more of the infused oil.

Remove from heat. Once mixture has come to room temperature, add oat flour. Mix by hand or with an immersion blender until incorporated.

Pour individual portions into appropriate containers and label.

Store in a cool, dark place for up to 1 year.

# Lanolin Salve

*Adapted from Rebecca Dillon (Dillon. 2013).*

## INGREDIENTS

1 tbsp beeswax

¼ cup lanolin, shea butter, or cocoa butter

½ tbsp (0.25 fl oz) pumpkin seed oil

½ tbsp (0.25 fl oz) almond, grapeseed, or olive oil infused with calendula (*Calendula officinalis*) flower

⅛ tsp vitamin E oil

⅛ tsp rosemary extract

The lanolin in this recipe provides a thick barrier that helps protect and soothe dry or irritated skin, and it also helps to draw moisture into the skin. If you can't find pumpkin seed oil, simply omit and double the amount of almond, grapeseed, or olive oil.

## DIRECTIONS

Make the calendula-infused oil using the instructions in the herb-infused oil tutorial. Note that ½ tablespoon is the amount of finished herbal oil to include in the recipe—you may need to start with more oil when making the herb-infused oil, as the herbs will soak up some of the oil (if you forget to do this, just top off with some plain oil as needed for this recipe). For practicality's sake, it makes sense to make a larger batch of calendula-infused oil than just the amount needed for this recipe!

Heat beeswax in a double boiler (or a glass or ceramic bowl or canning jar over a small saucepan of simmering water) until completely melted. Add lanolin, shea butter, or cocoa butter and stir until melted. Add almond and pumpkin seed oil and give a few stirs until everything is melted.

Dip a clean spoon into the formula and place it into a refrigerator so the salve will cool quickly and you can determine if its consistency is what you desire. If the sample is too soft, add a little more wax to the warm salve; if the sample is too hard, add a little more of the oil. Remove from heat.

Pour into tin(s) or jar(s) and let cool completely before capping and labeling. If using pumpkin seed oil, this salve is best refrigerated or used within 6 months, since pumpkin seed oil can easily oxidize. Otherwise, salve will last approximately 1 year.

CHAPTER FOURTEEN

# SCRUBS

# SCRUBS

Exfoliating treatments are fantastic for removing dead skin cells and blackheads. A gentle scrub can help to soften and balance the skin and promote blood circulation and lymphatic flow.

Stronger exfoliants can be fantastic for smoothing the rough skin of the feet, knees, or elbows, and an all-over sugar scrub can leave your skin feeling totally renewed. Try our gentler scrubs on the delicate facial skin, where a little exfoliation goes a long way!

# Vanilla
## LIP SCRUB

A lip scrub is just the thing to scrub away dead skin cells and deliver moisture back to tired wintertime lips. Use this vanilla lip scrub year-round before applying lipstick or lip balm—you might even notice your chosen lip cosmetic stays on longer, too!

---

### INGREDIENTS

FOR VANILLA SUGAR:

¼ cup sugar

¼ vanilla
(*Vanilla planifolia*) bean

FOR LIP SCRUB:

1 tsp vanilla sugar

½ tsp castor oil

½ tsp sweet almond oil

### DIRECTIONS

First, you'll make vanilla sugar (make a larger batch to have on hand for other body care products or baking!). Split the ¼ vanilla bean lengthwise and scoop out the seeds. Place the seeds, along with the sugar, in a spice grinder and grind until seeds are evenly dispersed. Transfer to a glass jar and cap tightly.

For best results, let the sugar and vanilla seeds sit overnight or longer.

Combine 1 teaspoon vanilla sugar and oils in a small bowl.

Apply a small amount to your lips, rubbing in a circular motion with your index finger.

Let sit for a few minutes on your lips.

Rinse off, pat dry, and apply lip balm or lipstick.

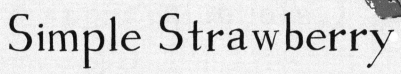

# Simple Strawberry
## ⁖ + Sage Scrub ⁖

### INGREDIENTS

⅓ cup strawberries

1 tbsp sage (*Salvia officinalis*) leaf powder

1 tsp raw honey (optional)

### DIRECTIONS

Slice strawberries thinly for ease with the next step.

With a mortar and pestle or similar tool such as a
small mixing bowl and fork, crush the strawberries into
a pulp along with the sage powder.

Optionally, add a teaspoon of honey or more
to your desired consistency.

Apply to clean skin by patting on. You may need to lie
on a towel or use in the shower or bath as it is slippery and drippy.

Leave on for 5-10 minutes.

Rinse face with warm water. Gently pat skin lightly
with a towel to dry.

Follow with moisturizer.

Strawberry seeds provide an exfoliant while the astringency,
enzymes, and hydration of the strawberries brighten skin. Sage is a
drying and slightly antiseptic component that's especially good for
oily or blemish-prone skin or for use in the summer. Additionally,
you can eat the remaining or drippy portions! The strawberries
and sage are the heart of this scrub, but for more hydration or a
smoother consistency, you may want to add a little honey.

# Calendula Sugar
## ᴖSCRUBᴖ

### INGREDIENTS

½ cup (4 fl oz) coconut oil

½ cup (4 fl oz) sweet almond or grapeseed oil

½ cup calendula (*Calendula officinalis*) flower

2 cups cane sugar

20-30 drops essential oil of choice (optional)

### DIRECTIONS

Combine the coconut oil, sweet almond oil, and calendula in a double boiler over low heat (or a glass or ceramic bowl or canning jar over a small saucepan of simmering water), and let infuse for 4 hours, stirring occasionally, and monitoring the temperature with a candy thermometer to be certain it stays below 140 degrees F.

Remove from heat and strain the calendula-infused oil. (If desired, you can leave the calendula petals in the oil, just be sure to use a drain strainer in the shower!)

In a bowl, combine calendula-infused oil and essential oil (if using) and stir thoroughly.

Add sugar and stir to combine.

Label, and store in a glass jar in a cool, dark place for up to 6-12 months.

Use as an all-over body scrub during a bath or shower. Do be careful as the oil from the scrub will make for a slippery tub, and be sure to wipe down the tub after use.

This sugar scrub exfoliates and offers the moisturizing, anti-inflammatory goodness of skin-friendly calendula-infused herbal oil. Some nice options for essential oils include lavender (*Lavandula* spp.), helichrysum (*Helichrysum italicum*), sustainably sourced frankincense (*Boswellia* spp.), and sweet orange (*Citrus* x *sinensis*).

# GENTLE OAT AND LAVENDER
## BODY SCRUB

Some body scrubs can be too exfoliating and drying for sensitive or dry skin—this gentle scrub uses ground oats and a small amount of sugar balanced with a nourishing oil for just the right amount of exfoliation for sensitive skin or skin that is new to scrubs!

### INGREDIENTS

¼ cup oats

4 tsp sugar

2 tsp lavender (*Lavandula* spp.) flower bud

¼ cup (2 fl oz) jojoba oil or camellia seed oil

### DIRECTIONS

Grind oats, sugar, and lavender into a powder using a spice grinder.

Combine powder with oil and stir well.

Apply a small amount to your skin, and scrub in a circular motion.

Rinse with warm water, and gently pat skin dry with a towel.

Do be careful as the oil/butter from the scrub will make for a slippery tub, and be sure to wipe down the tub afterwards.

# GROUNDING FOOT SCRUB

For feet that have been doing the tiresome job of keeping you moving all day, why not combine nourishing exfoliation with a relaxing aromatherapeutic blend grounded with a vetiver base note?

### INGREDIENTS

¾ cup finely ground sea salt

¼ cup coarsely ground sea salt

½ cup (4 fl oz) sesame or sweet almond oil or an herb-infused oil

8 drops bergamot (*Citrus* x *bergamia*) essential oil

8 drops geranium (*Pelargonium* spp.) essential oil

4 drops vetiver (*Vetiveria zizanioides*) essential oil

### DIRECTIONS

Pour oil into a bowl and add essential oils. Stir to combine.

Mix in salts.

Label, and store in a glass jar in a cool, dark place for 6–12 months.

To use, apply a few tablespoons of scrub to each foot, then work into skin while massaging feet.

Rinse with warm water and dry feet with a towel.

# MICRO-EXFOLIATING SCRUB

*Adapted from* Glow: The Nutritional Approach to Naturally Gorgeous Skin *by Nadia Neumann (Neumann, 2017).*

## INGREDIENTS

2 tsp baking soda

½ tsp aloe (*Aloe vera*) leaf gel

¼ tsp vegetable glycerin or herbal glycerite

## DIRECTIONS

Combine all ingredients in a small bowl
to form a paste.

Use your fingertips to gently massage the mixture
into facial skin, avoiding the eyes.

Rinse face with warm water. Gently pat skin
dry with a clean towel.

Follow with toner and moisturizer.

This scrub is best used no more than once a week.

---

This simple at-home scrub uses the fine particles of baking soda to slough off dead skin cells, leaving your skin bright and refreshed. Because baking soda has an alkaline pH, it's important to follow this with a gentle toner, such as rose water, to restore the skin's normal acidity and avoid irritating the skin. If you have very sensitive skin, try a patch test first.

# ROSEMARY CITRUS
# Foot Scrub

*Adapted from Kristy Doubet Haare on the Herbal Academy blog (Doubet Haare. 2018).*

A peppy, exfoliating pick-me-up for the feet!

## INGREDIENTS

1 cup fine sea salt

½ cup coarse pink Himalayan sea salt

2 tbsp (1 fl oz) lemon juice

2 tbsp (1 fl oz) grapefruit juice

2 tbsp (1 fl oz) fractionated coconut oil, olive oil,
or sweet almond oil

6 drops rosemary (*Rosmarinus officinalis*) essential oil

2 tbsp grapefruit (*Citrus x paradisi*) peel zest

1 tbsp lemon (*Citrus x limon*) peel zest

1 sprig rosemary (*Rosmarinus officinalis*)

## DIRECTIONS

Combine salts in a bowl. Add grapefruit and lemon juices
and stir to combine.

In a small container, combine coconut oil with rosemary
essential oil and mix thoroughly. Stir this mixture into the salts.

Add citrus peel and rosemary sprig and give a final stir.

To use, scoop up a handful of salts and massage into each
foot, using your thumb to work it into the cuticles.

Wrap each foot in a warm, moist hand towel, sit back, and
close your eyes for 5-10 minutes. Rinse each foot
with warm water and pat dry.

Store excess foot scrub in an airtight container,
label, and use within 1-2 weeks.

# Creamy Rose
## AND HONEY SKIN SCRUB

*Adapted from* 100 Organic Skincare Recipes *by Jessica Ress (Ress. 2014).*

Part scrub, part mask, this all-over body scrub will leave you glowing! Use fresh roses when they're in season for a euphoric sensory experience, but dry rose petals will work just fine, too. This works best if you make a fresh batch for each use. Prepare the scrub before getting into the bath or shower, then apply to warm, damp skin.

## INGREDIENTS

½ cup fresh or ¼ cup dry rose (*Rosa* spp.) petal

½ cup (4 fl oz) raw honey

¾ cup (6 fl oz) whole milk, cream, or coconut cream

1 cup almond meal

## DIRECTIONS

Combine rose petals, honey, and cream in a blender or food processor and mix into a smooth paste.

Use a flexible spatula to scrape the rose-honey cream into a bowl, then stir in the almond meal and mix thoroughly. Adjust the consistency as needed, adding more almond meal or honey to create a thick, spreadable paste.

Enjoy a warm bath or shower and then gently pat off extra water. You'll want to apply scrub to slightly damp skin. Working from the feet up, spread the skin scrub gently over the entire body, finishing with the face.

Using a gentle circular motion, massage the scrub into your skin, working from the legs up to the torso, then along the arms, moving from the hands toward the heart. Massage very gently into the skin of the face.

Leave in place as a whole-body mask for 15-30 minutes, relaxing in a warm area.

Rinse off in the shower using warm water.

# Vanilla and Rose
## BROWN SUGAR BODY SCRUB

*Adapted from* 101 Easy Homemade Products for Your Skin, Health, & Home
*by Jan Berry (Berry. 2016a).*

## INGREDIENTS

1½ tbsp (0.75 fl oz)
vanilla (*Vanilla planifolia*) seed-
and
rose (*Rosa* spp.) petal-
infused coconut oil

2 tbsp shea butter or
cocoa butter

½ tbsp (0.25 fl oz)
raw honey

¼ cup
brown sugar

## DIRECTIONS

Make the vanilla- and rose-infused coconut oil using the instructions in the herb-infused oil tutorial. For each 1 cup coconut oil, use 1 vanilla bean, split, and ¼ cup rose petals.

Combine the vanilla-rose coconut oil and shea (or cocoa) butter in a double boiler over low heat (or a glass or ceramic bowl or canning jar over a small saucepan of simmering water), stirring occasionally until completely melted. Once melted, remove from heat.

Add honey and brown sugar, then stir well to combine.

Transfer mixture to candy/soap molds or an ice cube tray.

Place in freezer until solid, then remove from molds/tray.

Store in a glass jar in the refrigerator for 6-12 months.

Use 1 or 2 cubes as a body scrub in the bath or shower. These feel especially nice on rough elbows and heels!

Do be careful as the oil/butter from the scrub will make for a slippery tub, and be sure to wipe down the tub afterwards.

This decadent body scrub is a delight to the senses!

CHAPTER FIFTEEN

# SERUMS

# SERUMS

Serums can be applied to help address your primary skin concerns, whether that's brightening the skin, lightening dark spots or circles, or adding extra anti-inflammatory support to help calm and nourish. These serums all incorporate deeply nourishing seed oils that are rich in unsaturated fatty acids, which help to decrease inflammation and create glowing, supple skin.

# ROSE HELICHRYSUM
## Skin Serum

This serum supports skin healing to reduce scarring. Infusing rose (*Rosa* spp.) into jojoba oil takes this serum to the next level!

### INGREDIENTS

2 tbsp (1 fl oz) jojoba oil or jojoba oil infused with rose (*Rosa* spp.) petal

1 tbsp (0.5 fl oz) rosehip seed oil

1 tbsp (0.5 fl oz) baobab oil

3 drops helichrysum (*Helichrysum italicum*) essential oil

3 drops Roman chamomile (*Chamaemelum nobile*) or German chamomile (*Matricaria chamomilla*) essential oil

### DIRECTIONS

Make the rose-infused oil using the instructions in the herb-infused oil tutorial.

Combine ingredients in a 2-ounce glass bottle and shake to combine.

Label, and store in a cool, dark place for up to 1 year.

Use daily after cleansing routine.
A little goes a long way!

# MOISTURIZING
## *Facial Serum*

*Adapted from Alice Duvernell (Duvernell. 2010).*

A moisturizing facial serum for day and night use.

## INGREDIENTS

WATER PHASE:

4½ tbsp (2.25 fl oz) water and/or hydrosol of your choice (e.g., rose (*Rosa* spp.), chamomile (*Matricaria chamomilla*), neroli (*Citrus* x *aurantium*))

2 tbsp (1 fl oz) aloe (*Aloe vera*) leaf juice

1 tbsp (0.5 fl oz) vegetable glycerin or herbal glycerite

¼ tsp adragante or agar-agar gum

OIL PHASE:

1 tbsp (0.5 fl oz) oil and/or herb-infused oil

9-12 drops essential oil of choice

6 drops rosemary (*Rosmarinus officinalis*) oleoresin extract

## DIRECTIONS

Using a glass measuring cup or 500-milliliter beaker, combine the hydrosol/water, aloe juice, and glycerin/glycerite; stir until blended.

Add the gum and mix with a mini hand mixer or immersion blender until fully dissolved. Note: if using agar-agar, introduce it to the water phase and boil for 2 minutes for best results. Allow this to cool to below 120 degrees F before combining with the oil phase.

In a separate glass measuring cup or 50-milliliter beaker, combine all of the ingredients in the oil phase and stir until blended.

Pour the oil phase blend into the waters and gum mixture and blend with a mini hand mixer or immersion blender until all ingredients are completely blended and the color is uniform.

Transfer to a glass bottle with dropper top, label, and store in refrigerator for up to 3 months.

Use day and night on dry, mature, and/or damaged skin. As it dries it may tighten a bit, so lightly massage your face once dried.

# LUXURIOUS
# *Floral Facial Serum*

A luxurious blend of face-friendly oils and hydrating floral waters, this recipe will be sure to give your skin the goodness it deserves.

## *INGREDIENTS*

### WATER PHASE:

2 tbsp (1 fl oz) floral hydrosol
(e.g., lavender (*Lavandula* spp.), rose (*Rosa* spp.),
geranium (*Pelargonium* spp.))

⅔ tsp aloe (*Aloe vera*) leaf juice

⅔ tsp tincture (e.g., calendula (*Calendula officinalis*) flower,
gotu kola (*Centella asiatica*) leaf, echinacea (*Echinacea* spp.) root)

⅛ tsp xanthan gum

### OIL PHASE:

⅔ tsp carrier oil(s) (e.g., safflower, sunflower, olive, apricot)

½ tsp rosehip seed, evening primrose seed, black cumin seed,
or borage seed oil

10 drops essential oil (optional)

## *DIRECTIONS*

Using a glass measuring cup or 100-milliliter beaker,
combine the hydrosol, aloe juice, and tincture; stir until blended.

Add the xanthan gum and mix with a mini hand mixer or immersion
blender until fully dissolved. To avoid clumping, sprinkle a little bit
of the xanthan gum on the surface of the liquid at a time,
mixing in between additions.

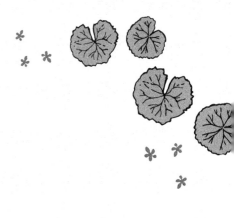

In a separate glass measuring cup or 50-milliliter beaker, combine all of the oil phase ingredients and stir until blended.

Pour oil phase blend into the water and xanthan gum mixture, and mix with a mini hand mixer or immersion blender until all ingredients are completely blended and the color is uniform.

Transfer serum to a glass bottle with dropper top, label, and store in refrigerator for up to 3 months.

Use day and night on dry, mature, and/or damaged skin. As it dries it may tighten a bit, so lightly massage your face once dried.

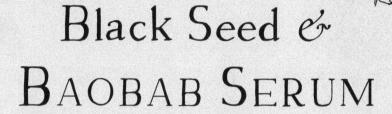

# Black Seed &
# Baobab Serum

## INGREDIENTS

1 tbsp (0.5 fl oz) rosehip seed oil

1 tbsp (0.5 fl oz) black seed oil

2 tbsp (1 fl oz) baobab seed oil

6 drops Roman chamomile (*Chamaemelum nobile*),
German chamomile (*Matricaria chamomilla*),
or helichrysum (*Helichrysum italicum*) essential oil (optional)

## DIRECTIONS

Combine all ingredients in a 2-ounce glass bottle with pump or dropper top; shake well. Be sure to label!

Use as a daily moisturizer to soothe the skin. After cleansing, apply a small amount of oil to damp skin morning and night.

Store in a cool, dry place for up to 1 year.

This nourishing facial serum combines powerhouse anti-inflammatory base oils with gentle and calming essential oils that make it ideal for reddened, couperose skin. Most people will benefit from helichrysum and chamomile essential oils, especially at the low concentration used in this recipe; however, if you have extremely sensitive skin, do try a patch test first, or simply omit the essential oils.

# Coffee Rose
## UNDEREYE SERUM

Moisturizing, astringent, and stimulating to circulation, this serum can be helpful for dark circles and puffy undereye skin.

### INGREDIENTS

2 tbsp coffee (*Coffea* spp.) bean, coarsely ground

1 tbsp rose (*Rosa* spp.) petal

4 tbsp (2 fl oz) sweet almond or jojoba oil

2 tbsp (1 fl oz) rosehip seed oil

### DIRECTIONS

Following the directions for making an infused herbal oil, infuse the coffee grounds and rose petals into almond or jojoba oil.

After straining, add rosehip seed oil.

Transfer to a dropper bottle or a roller ball applicator.

Label, and store in the refrigerator for up to 6 months.

To use, gently dab a few drops of serum under eye areas each morning and night before bed.

# Soothing
## SKIN SERUM

This ultra-nourishing and anti-inflammatory skin serum
is a gift for irritated skin.

### INGREDIENTS

2 tbsp (1 fl oz) jojoba
oil infused with lavender
(*Lavandula* spp.) flower bud

1 tbsp (0.5 fl oz) rosehip
seed oil

1 tbsp (0.5 fl oz)
marula oil

### DIRECTIONS

Make a lavender-infused oil using
the instructions in the herb-infused
oil tutorial.

Combine ingredients in a 2-ounce
glass dropper bottle and shake well.

Label, and store in a cool, dark
place for up to 1 year.

Apply a few drops to skin after
cleansing. A little goes a long way!

# Rosemary
## EYEBROW SERUM

*Adapted from* An Atlas of Natural Beauty: Botanical Ingredients for
Retaining and Enhancing Beauty *by Victoire de Taillac and Ramdane
Touhami (de Taillac & Touhami. 2018).*

For eyebrows thick enough to color, try this eyebrow growth serum!

### INGREDIENTS

1 tsp castor oil

1 tsp rosemary
(*Rosmarinus officinalis*)
aerial parts tincture

### DIRECTIONS

Combine both ingredients in
a bowl or jar and whisk until
combined.

Without getting too close to the
eyes, massage the eyebrows with
this preparation for 1 minute or
more.

# Elderflower
# SERUM

*Adapted from* Alchemy of Herbs *by Rosalee de la Forêt (de la Forêt. 2017).*

This silky, soothing oil can help protect against UVA radiation damage and feels lovely to boot! Take note, this should not be used as a sunscreen; instead, apply it morning and evening as a daily moisturizer in addition to your regular sun protection.

## INGREDIENTS

½ cup (4 fl oz) jojoba oil (or other carrier oil of your choice)

¼ cup elder (*Sambucus nigra* or *S. canadensis*) flower

¼ cup calendula (*Calendula officinalis*) flower

1 tsp rosemary extract or ¼ tsp vitamin E oil

10-15 drops essential oil of choice (optional)

## DIRECTIONS

Make the elder- and calendula-infused oil using the instructions in the herb-infused oil tutorial.

Once the oil has been infused and strained, stir in the rosemary extract (or vitamin E oil) and essential oil, if using.

Store in a glass bottle with pump or dropper top for up to 1 year. Don't forget to label!

After cleansing your face in the morning and evening, apply one to two pumps or droppers to damp skin and massage in gently.

CHAPTER SIXTEEN

# SOAPS

# SOAPS

The art of soapmaking is enjoying a renaissance, and once you get started making your own herbal soaps, you'll see why! It doesn't take a lot of fancy equipment, and mastering a few basic steps and precautions will allow you to make any kind of soap you can dream up, from creamy facial milk bars to liquid laundry soap. Start with these well-tested recipes as you're building up your soapmaking chops—from there, the sky's the limit!

Note that all soap recipe ingredients, including essential oils, are measured by weight, not volume, unless otherwise noted.

# Everyday Soap Recipe

This soap recipe is great for most skin types.
Amount: 3 pounds or 12 4-ounce bars
Lye discount: 5%

## INGREDIENTS

15 oz olive oil

9 oz coconut oil

4 oz cocoa butter

3 oz apricot kernel oil

2 oz sweet almond oil

12.5 oz distilled water

4.7 oz lye

1 oz essential oil of choice

## DIRECTIONS

Prepare mold, lining it if necessary.

Weigh and combine the olive oil, coconut oil, cocoa butter, apricot kernel oil, and sweet almond oil in a large stainless steel pot. Heat until melted and cool to 90-110 degrees F.

Weigh the distilled water and lye. Go outside and with proper safety gear on, add the lye to the water, stirring until dissolved. Cool to 90-110 degrees F.

After oils and lye water are cooled, pour lye water into oils and blend with an immersion blender on and off until the mixture reaches light to medium trace.

Add essential oil and blend until incorporated.

Pour into mold, cover, and insulate for 24 hours.

Remove from mold, cut, and cure for 4-6 weeks.

# Nettle & Goat Milk
## SHAMPOO BAR

Nettle helps to regulate oil production, reduce inflammation, and encourage skin healing.
Amount: 3 pounds or 12 4-ounce bars; Lye discount: 15%

### INGREDIENTS

16 oz distilled water

2 cups fresh nettle (*Urtica dioica*) leaf or 1 teaspoon dried nettle leaf powder

11 oz olive oil

10 oz coconut oil

5 oz castor oil

4 oz avocado oil

2 oz shea butter

4 oz goat milk

4 oz lye

0.5 oz rosemary (*Rosmarinus officinalis*) essential oil

0.5 oz eucalyptus (*Eucalyptus globulus*) essential oil

0.3 oz lemon (*Citrus x limon*) essential oil

### DIRECTIONS

Prepare mold, lining it if necessary.

Heat distilled water to boiling point. Remove from heat and add fresh or dried nettle. Allow to cool. Remove nettle or strain out powdered nettle. Measure out 8 ounces of nettle infusion, add goat milk, and put into the freezer until slushy and almost frozen.

Weigh and combine the olive oil, coconut oil, castor oil, avocado oil, and shea butter in a large stainless steel pot. Heat until melted and cool to 90–110 degrees F.

Weigh lye. Go outside, and with proper safety gear on, add lye to the goat milk and nettle water mixture, stirring until dissolved. Cool to 90–110 degrees F.

After oils and lye water are cooled, pour lye water into oils and blend with an immersion blender on and off until the mixture reaches light trace.

Add essential oils and blend until incorporated.

Pour into mold, cover, and insulate lightly for 24 hours. Goat milk can cause soap to overheat so watch for any bubbling or splitting. If gel becomes too dark, remove cover.

Remove from mold, cut, and cure for 4–6 weeks.

# Gentle
## DOWN-TO-EARTH
## SOAP

A gentle bar with an earthy scent that is grounding and uplifting.
Amount: 3 pounds or 12 4-ounce bars
Lye discount: 15%

## INGREDIENTS

18 oz olive oil

8 oz coconut oil

5 oz castor oil

3 oz cocoa butter

2 oz shea butter

12.5 oz distilled water

4.4 oz lye

0.5 oz frankincense
(*Boswellia* spp.) essential
oil, sustainably sourced

0.3 oz cedarwood (*Cedrus atlantica*) essential oil

0.3 oz lemon (*Citrus x limon*) essential oil

## DIRECTIONS

Prepare mold, lining it if necessary.

Weigh and combine the olive oil, coconut oil, castor oil, cocoa butter, and shea butter in a large stainless steel pot. Heat until melted and cool to 90–110 degrees F.

Weigh the distilled water and lye. Go outside, and with proper safety gear on, add the lye to the water, stirring until dissolved. Cool to 90–110 degrees F.

After oils and lye water are cooled, pour lye water into oils and blend with an immersion blender on and off until the mixture reaches light to medium trace.

Add essential oils and blend until incorporated.

Pour into mold, cover, and insulate for 24 hours.

Remove from mold, cut, and cure for 4–6 weeks.

# Floral Delight
## SOAP

A hard, bubbly, floral-scented soap.
Amount: 3 pounds or 12 4-ounce bars
Lye discount: 10%

## INGREDIENTS

10 oz olive oil

10 oz tallow (or cocoa butter, mango butter, or shea butter)

9 oz coconut oil

3 oz avocado oil

12 oz distilled water

4.4 oz lye

2 tsp rose clay (optional)

0.5 oz rose (*Rosa* spp.) essential oil

0.5 oz geranium (*Pelargonium* spp.) essential oil

2 tbsp dried rose (*Rosa* spp.) petal

## DIRECTIONS

Prepare mold, lining it if necessary.

Weigh and combine the olive oil, tallow, coconut oil, and avocado oil in a large stainless steel pot. Heat until melted and cool to 90–110 degrees F.

Weigh the distilled water and lye. Go outside, and with proper safety gear on, add lye to the water, stirring until dissolved. Cool to 90–110 degrees F.

After oils and lye water are cooled, pour lye water into oils and blend with an immersion blender on and off until the mixture reaches light to medium trace.

Add essential oils and rose clay and blend until incorporated.

Pour into mold. Sprinkle rose petals over the top. Using a gloved hand, lightly press petals into the top. Cover and insulate for 24 hours.

Remove from mold, cut, and cure for 4–6 weeks.

# Soothing
## MOISTURE-RICH
# Body Bar

The coconut milk, honey, and superfat content of this recipe help to create a very moisturizing full-body bar.

Amount: 3 pounds or 12 4-ounce bars

Lye discount: 15%

## INGREDIENTS

8 oz distilled water

5.5 oz canned full-fat coconut milk

4.4 oz lye

18 oz olive oil

6 oz tallow (or cocoa butter, mango butter, or shea butter)

5 oz coconut oil

5 oz castor oil

2 oz mango butter

2 tsp raw honey

1 oz lavender (*Lavandula* spp.) essential oil

2 tbsp lavender (*Lavandula* spp.) flower bud (optional)

## DIRECTIONS

Prepare mold, lining it if necessary.

Weigh the distilled water, coconut milk, and lye. Combine the water and coconut milk and place in the freezer until slushy and almost frozen. (This will keep the sugars in the milk from scorching when you add the lye.) Go outside, and with proper safety gear on, add the lye to the coconut milk water, stirring until dissolved.

Cool to 90–110 degrees F.

Weigh and combine the olive oil, tallow, coconut oil, castor oil, and mango butter in a large stainless steel pot. Heat until melted and cool to 90–110 degrees F.

After oils and lye water are cooled, pour lye water into oils and blend with an immersion blender on and off until the mixture reaches light to medium trace.

Add essential oil and honey and blend until incorporated.

Pour into mold. Sprinkle lavender flowers over the top, if desired. Using a gloved hand, lightly press lavender into the top. Cover and insulate lightly for 24 hours.

Remove from mold, cut, and cure for 4–6 weeks.

# Cinnamon, Oats, and Honey
## EXFOLIATING BAR

Blended oats create gentle exfoliation, while honey adds moisture and bubbles in this nut-free soap. Use this as a base recipe for individuals with nut allergies.

Amount: 3 pounds or 12 4-ounce bars

Lye discount: 15%

## INGREDIENTS

15 oz olive oil

8 oz babassu oil

6 oz castor oil

3 oz cocoa butter

3 oz shea butter

13 oz distilled water

4.25 oz lye

1 tbsp raw honey

½ cup blended oats

0.3 oz cinnamon (*Cinnamomum* spp.) leaf essential oil

## DIRECTIONS

Prepare mold, lining it if necessary.

Weigh and combine the olive oil, babassu oil, castor oil, cocoa butter, and shea butter in a large stainless steel pot. Heat until melted and cool to 90–110 degrees F.

Weigh the distilled water and lye. Go outside, and with proper safety gear on, add the lye to the water, stirring until dissolved. Cool to 90–110 degrees F.

After oils and lye water are cooled, pour lye water into oils and blend with an immersion blender on and off until the mixture reaches light to medium trace.

Add raw honey, oats, and essential oil and blend until incorporated.

Pour into mold and cover.
Sprinkle with additional steel cut oats on top if desired.
Insulate lightly for 24 hours.

Remove from mold, cut, and cure for 4–6 weeks.

# Acne Charcoal
# SOAP

Activated charcoal and tea tree essential oil provide a deeply
cleansing and antibacterial soap.
Amount: 3 pounds or 12 4-ounce bars
Lye discount: 10%

## INGREDIENTS

20 oz olive oil

9 oz coconut oil

3 oz cocoa butter

12 oz distilled water

4.3 oz lye

2 tsp activated charcoal powder

1 oz tea tree (*Melaleuca alternifolia*) essential oil

## DIRECTIONS

Prepare mold, lining it if necessary.

Weigh and combine the olive oil, coconut oil, and cocoa butter in a large
stainless steel pot. Heat until melted and cool to 90-110 degrees F.

Weigh the distilled water and lye. Go outside, and with proper safety gear on,
add the lye to the water, stirring until dissolved. Cool to 90-110 degrees F.

After oils and lye water are cooled, pour lye water into oils and blend with an
immersion blender on and off until the mixture reaches light to medium trace.

Add essential oil and activated charcoal powder and blend until incorporated.

Pour into mold, cover, and insulate for 24 hours.

Remove from mold, cut, and cure for 4-6 weeks.

# Laundry Bar

Laundry bars need a very low superfat content so that your washing machine does not become clogged and clothes come out clean. This laundry bar is perfect for fine shredding with a cheese grater and adding to one part baking soda and one part borax for a natural laundry soap that really works.

Amount: 3 pounds or 12 4-ounce bars

Lye discount: 1%

## INGREDIENTS

24 oz coconut oil

10 oz olive oil

12.5 oz distilled water

5.7 oz lye

0.5 oz lavender (*Lavandula* spp.) essential oil

0.5 oz lemon (*Citrus x limon*) essential oil

## DIRECTIONS

Prepare mold, lining it if necessary.

Weigh and combine the coconut oil and olive oil in a large stainless steel pot. If coconut oil is solid, heat until melted and cool to 90-110 degrees F.

Weigh the water and lye. Go outside, and with proper safety gear on, add lye to the water, stirring until dissolved. Cool to 90-110 degrees F.

After oils and lye water are cooled, pour lye water into oils and blend with an immersion blender on and off until the mixture reaches light to medium trace.

Add essential oils and blend until incorporated.

Pour into mold and insulate for 24 hours.

Remove from mold, cut, and cure for 4-6 weeks.

Shred one bar very finely and add to 2 pounds baking soda and 2 pounds borax. Mix thoroughly.

Start water in washing machine and add ½ cup laundry soap mixture before adding clothes.

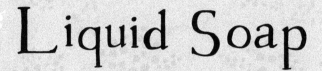

# Liquid Soap

Making liquid soap that has the perfect thickness and texture every time can be challenging—liquid soap may not thicken appropriately, or it may thicken and bond together so strongly that the soap develops an unpleasantly stringy, snot-like texture.

Carefully follow the instructions below for a dependable liquid soap.

## INGREDIENTS
4 4-ounce soap bars

1 gallon (128 fl oz) distilled water

## DIRECTIONS
Heat distilled water in a large pot over medium heat.

Grate four 4-ounce bars of soap of your choice with a cheese grater into the hot water and stir gently until melted.

Remove from heat and allow to cool to room temperature.

Wait until the liquid has thickened (this may take 1-2 weeks), and then use an immersion blender to blend until desired consistency. Alternatively, freeze immediately after cooling until it becomes semi-solid and then allow to return to room temperature. Once at room temperature, blend with an immersion blender.

Store in a 1-gallon container. If it thickens too much or bonds together again, repeat the blending step.

Because this liquid soap contains water, it's recommended to include a preservative to extend shelf life; be sure to choose a preservative that is suited for the higher pH of soap and follow the manufacturer's instructions for adding to the recipe.

CHAPTER SEVENTEEN

# SPRAYS

# SPRAYS

As a fragrant body mist, hydrating facial spritz, or soothing relief for sunburn, herbal body sprays are incredibly easy to make and infinitely handy. Some of these recipes are more at home in your first aid kit, while others are ideal for daily facial care—and since they take just a few minutes to put together, you might want to keep them all on hand!

# YARROW AND PALMAROSA
## Skin Spray

Yarrow and palmarosa are both anti-inflammatory, antimicrobial, and cooling in nature; combined with soothing aloe gel, this skin spray may help to ease the discomfort of rosacea. Note that a thick aloe gel (not an aloe juice) is needed to serve as a carrier if essential oil is included in the recipe.

### INGREDIENTS

½ cup (4 fl oz) infusion of yarrow (*Achillea millefolium*) aerial parts made with distilled water

2 tbsp (1 fl oz) thick aloe (*Aloe vera*) leaf gel

1 tbsp (0.5 fl oz) yarrow (*Achillea millefolium*) tincture

15 drops palmarosa (*Cymbopogon martinii*) essential oil

Natural preservative (optional)

### DIRECTIONS

Prepare the yarrow infusion by combining 2 tablespoons yarrow with ½ cup distilled water fresh off the boil, and steep for 20 minutes, covered.

Combine ingredients well by shaking gently in a spray bottle.

Label, and store in the refrigerator for up to 3 days (if using a preservative, shelf life will be longer).

Use in place of toner after cleansing skin. Shake well before applying.

# Cucumber, Aloe, & Rose Facial Spritz

### INGREDIENTS

¼ cup (2 fl oz) rose (*Rosa* spp.) hydrosol

1 tsp aloe (*Aloe vera*) leaf juice

2 slices fresh cucumber
(approximately ¼ inch thick), peeled

### DIRECTIONS

Place all ingredients in a blender and blend
until smooth.

Strain through a tea strainer or cheesecloth to
remove cucumber pulp.

Pour into a spray-top glass bottle and store in
refrigerator for up to 1 week.

Spritz on to skin as needed.

This delightfully cooling spray can be applied for flushing, as
a toner for rosacea-prone skin, or simply to cool the heat
of irritated or sun-exposed skin.

# Green Tea
# ACNE SPRAY

*Adapted from* Forgotten Ways for Modern Days *by Rachel Blondel*
*(Blondel. 2016).*

## INGREDIENTS

1 tea bag green tea (*Camellia sinensis*) leaf

1 tsp fresh ginger (*Zingiber officinale*) rhizome, grated

¼ cup (2 fl oz) distilled water

1½ tbsp (0.75 fl oz) apple cider vinegar

1 tbsp (0.5 fl oz) vegetable glycerin

Natural preservative (optional)

## DIRECTIONS

Infuse the green tea and ginger in just-off-the boil water until cool.
Strain the infusion.

In a 4-ounce glass bottle with spray top, combine 3 tablespoons
infusion, vinegar, and glycerin, and shake to mix well. Add natural
preservative, if using.

Spray or dab onto acne spots.

Keeps for 1 week, refrigerated (if using a preservative, shelf life will
be longer).

**This toning spray can be applied to blemishes to help
support the skin's healing process.**

# Witch Hazel
## SKIN SPRAY

*Adapted from* Home Remedies for Psoriasis *by Kathi Keville and Karta Purkh Singh Khalsa (Keville & Khalsa. 2009).*

This is a soothing astringent spray with antimicrobial essential oils. Note that a thick aloe gel (not an aloe juice) is needed to serve as a carrier if essential oil is included in the recipe.

### INGREDIENTS

⅓ cup (2.7 fl oz) witch hazel (*Hamamelis virginiana*) bark extract

2 tbsp (1 fl oz) thick aloe (*Aloe vera*) leaf gel

¼ tsp vitamin E oil

15 drops tea tree (*Melaleuca alternifolia*) essential oil

10 drops lavender (*Lavandula* spp.) essential oil

5 drops clove (*Syzygium aromaticum*) essential oil

### DIRECTIONS

Add essential oils to a dark-colored glass bottle with a spray top. Be sure to label!

Add remaining ingredients and shake well.

To use, shake well, then mist onto skin.

Store in a cool, dark place for up to 6 months.

# Insect Repellant
## SPRAY

This is to be sprayed on clothes only (not directly on skin), as the essential oils aren't diluted in a carrier oil.

### INGREDIENTS

¾ cup (6 fl oz) catnip (*Nepeta cataria*) hydrosol

¼ cup (2 fl oz) 190-proof alcohol

35 drops lemon eucalyptus (*Eucalyptus citriodora*) essential oil

25 drops geranium (*Pelargonium* spp.) essential oil

20 drops Virginia cedarwood (*Juniperus virginiana*) essential oil

### DIRECTIONS

Combine all ingredients in an 8-ounce glass bottle with spray top.

Label, and store in a cool, dark place or refrigerator for up to 1 year.

Shake well before use.

# AFTER-SUN
## Spray

This cooling and protecting spray can be used directly after time in the sun, or as a soothing application for sunburn or other minor burns.

### INGREDIENTS

½ cup (4 fl oz) lavender (*Lavandula* spp.) hydrosol

¼ cup (2 fl oz) aloe (*Aloe vera*) leaf juice

¼ cup (2 fl oz) tulsi (*Ocimum tenuiflorum*) hydrosol

### DIRECTIONS

Combine aloe juice and hydrosol in a spray-top bottle, shake well, label, and store in the refrigerator for up to 6 months.

To use, spray directly on skin.

*By all means, do treat your skin to an herbal day spa every so often! But it's even more important to love your skin daily with a regular routine that supports normal skin pH, healthy microflora, and a balanced inflammatory response, which are foundations of skin health and function.*

BOTANICAL SKIN CARE COURSE

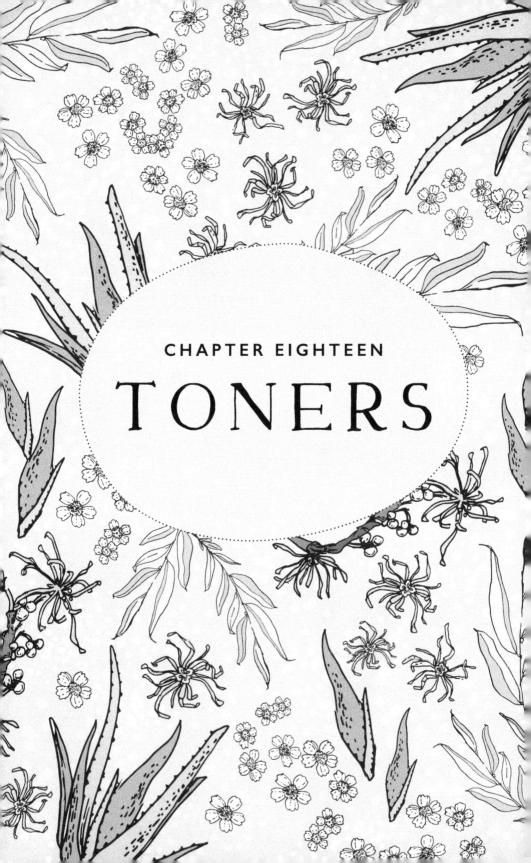

CHAPTER EIGHTEEN

# TONERS

# TONERS

Toners are an often-missed fundamental of skin care. By gently astringing the skin and restoring the proper pH, toners can help improve skin irritation, dryness, and acne, while gently firming the skin. Choose a toner that's right for your skin—more astringent and antimicrobial for oily skin, more soothing and hydrating for mature or dry skin— and apply after cleansing your face.

# *Hydrating Toner*
## For Mature Skin

### INGREDIENTS

½ cup (4 fl oz) helichrysum
(*Helichrysum italicum*) hydrosol

¼ cup (2 fl oz) geranium (*Pelargonium* spp.)
hydrosol

4 tsp vegetable glycerin

### DIRECTIONS

Combine ingredients in an 8-ounce glass bottle.

Label, and store in a cool, dark place or
refrigerator for up to 6 months.

Apply to skin, using a cotton ball or clean hands.

No need to be afraid of toners if you have dry
or mature skin! Try this gentle, hydrating toner
that combines soothing hydrosols
with a humectant.

# Calming Toner
## FOR INFLAMED SKIN

This delightful blend of skin-loving, anti-inflammatory hydrosols makes a great daily facial toner for inflammation-prone skin; it also doubles as a soothing spritz for sunburned or otherwise inflamed areas anywhere on the skin!

### INGREDIENTS

½ cup (4 fl oz) chamomile
(*Matricaria chamomilla*) hydrosol

¼ cup (2 fl oz) rose (*Rosa* spp.) hydrosol

¼ cup (2 fl oz) frankincense (*Boswellia* spp.)
hydrosol, sustainably sourced

### DIRECTIONS

Combine hydrosols in an 8-ounce glass bottle
with spray top.

Label, and store in a cool, dark place
or refrigerator for up to 6 months.

Spritz on inflamed skin.

# Aloe and Neroli
## DRY SKIN TONER

*Adapted from* Natural Beauty *by Karen Gilbert (Gilbert. 2013).*

A moisturizing skin toner to soothe dry or sensitive skin after washing.

### INGREDIENTS

2 tsp aloe (*Aloe vera*) leaf gel

5 tbsp (2.5 fl oz) neroli (*Citrus x aurantium*) hydrosol

½ tsp calendula (*Calendula officinalis*) flower tincture

½ tsp vegetable glycerin

### DIRECTIONS

Combine all ingredients in a 4-ounce glass bottle with a spray top.

Shake well to combine. Label, and store in the refrigerator for up to 6 months.

To use, mist over clean skin.

# Toning, Cooling Astringent
## FOR OILY, BLEMISHED SKIN

Designed to refresh blemished bodily and/or facial skin, this can be sprayed or wiped over sweaty, oily, or affected areas. It is especially nice in hot, humid weather!

### INGREDIENTS

¼ cup (2 fl oz) yarrow (*Achillea millefolium*) hydrosol

⅛ cup (1 fl oz) yarrow (*Achillea millefolium*) aerial parts tincture

⅛ cup (1 fl oz) witch hazel (*Hamamelis virginiana*) bark extract

### DIRECTIONS

Combine all ingredients in a 4-ounce glass bottle with a spray top.

Shake well to combine. Label, and store in the refrigerator for up to 6 months.

To use, mist over clean skin.

# Lavender and Witch Hazel Oily Skin Toner

*Adapted from Natural Beauty by Karen Gilbert (Gilbert. 2013).*

**An astringent skin toner to tone skin after washing.**

## INGREDIENTS

2 tsp witch hazel
(*Hamamelis virginiana*)
bark extract

5 tbsp (2.5 fl oz) lavender
(*Lavandula* spp.) hydrosol

½ tsp yarrow
(*Achillea millefolium*)
aerial parts tincture

½ tsp vegetable glycerin

## DIRECTIONS

Combine all ingredients in a 4-ounce glass bottle with a spray top.

Shake well to combine.

Label, and store in the refrigerator for up to 6 months.

To use, mist over clean skin.

# Simple Vinegar Skin Toner

This toner balances skin pH, while lavender or rose soothes and cools.

## INGREDIENTS

¼ cup (2 fl oz) apple
cider vinegar

½ cup (4 fl oz) lavender
(*Lavandula* spp.) or rose
(*Rosa* spp.) hydrosol

## DIRECTIONS

Combine vinegar and hydrosol of choice in an 8-ounce bottle with spray top.

Label, and store in a cool, dark place for up to 6 months.

Spray or dab onto skin after cleansing.

# Clarifying
## FACIAL TONER

Astringent and anti-inflammatory willow bark makes an excellent base for a facial toner. It works especially well for acne-prone skin, perhaps because of its salicylate content. Lavender and rose hydrosol both offer additional anti-inflammatory and vulnerary power, and depending on your preference, add a lovely scent as well!

---

### INGREDIENTS
¼ cup (2 fl oz)
well-strained willow
(*Salix nigra*) bark decoction
¼ cup (2 fl oz) lavender (*Lavandula* spp.)
or rose (*Rosa* spp.) hydrosol

### DIRECTIONS
Prepare decoction by simmering 2 tablespoons willow bark in ½ cup water for 20–30 minutes.
Let cool and strain.

Combine ¼ cup of the decoction and hydrosol in a spray-top bottle and store in the refrigerator for up to 1 week.

Spray directly on face or on a cloth or cotton ball and gently dab onto the skin.

*Holistic practices of skin care and cosmetic adornment are as ancient as humankind's longtime association of beauty with health and vitality.*

BOTANICAL SKIN CARE COURSE

# REFERENCES

Anthis, C. (2014a). Lice home remedies using herbs. Retrieved from https://theherbalacademy. com/lice-home-remedies-using-herbs/

Anthis, C. (2014b). Natural no-poo cleansers for healthy hair. Retrieved from http://www. thehippyhomemaker.com/natural-no-poo-cleansers-healthy-hair-natural-hair-care-series-part-2/

Berry, J. (2016a). *101 easy homemade products for your skin, health, & home.* Salem, MA: Page Street Publishing Co.

Berry, J. (2016b). Calendula bath melts & body butter recipes. Retrieved from https:// thenerdyfarmwife.com/calendula-bath-melts-body-butter-recipes/

Blondel, R. (2016). *Forgotten ways for modern days.* New York, NY: Tarcher Perigee.

Buck, S. (2014). *Natural beauty: 200 tips, techniques, and recipes for natural beauty.* Beverly, MA: Fair Winds Press.

Cable, K. (2014). 5 homemade shaving cream recipes. Retrieved from https://simplelifemom. com/2014/11/12/5-homemade-shaving-cream-recipes/

Codekas, C. (2018). *Healing herbal infusions.* Salem, MA: Page Street Publishing Co.

Crunchy Betty. (2019). Solving the world's deodorant crisis: A new soothing recipe. Retrieved from https://crunchybetty.com/solving-the-worlds-deodorant-crisis-a-new-soothing-recipe

de la Forêt, R. (2017). *Alchemy of herbs.* Carlsbad, CA: Hay House Publishing.

de Taillac, V., & Touhami, R. (2018). *An atlas of natural beauty: Botanical ingredients for retaining and enhancing beauty.* New York, NY: Simon & Schuster.

Dillon, R. (2013). Natural lanolin salve recipe for dry, damaged skin. Retrieved from http:// soapdelinews.com/2013/08/diy-handmade-natural-lanolin-salve-recipe.html

Dobrev, H. (2007). Clinical and instrumental study of the efficacy of a new sebum control cream. *Journal of Cosmetic Dermatology, 6*(2), 113-118. http://doi.org/10.1111/j.1473-2165.2007.00306.x

Doubet Haare, K. (2018). 3 steps for an herbal-infused pedicure for beautiful nails and soft feet. Retrieved from https://theherbalacademy.com/herbal-infused-pedicure/

Duvernell, A. (2009-2010). Facial serums: Luxury serums for natural cosmetology [class handout]. Richmond, CA.: The Nova Studio.

Galper, A., & Daigneault, C. (2018). *Plant-powered beauty.* Dallas, TX: BenBella Books, Inc.

Gerber, S. (2006). *Hello glow: 150+ easy natural beauty recipes for a fresh new you.* San Francisco, CA: Weldon Owen.

Gianni, A.M. (n.d.). Ditch the chemicals - 7 ways to color your hair naturally. Retrieved from https://www.annmariegianni.com/7-ways-to-color-your-hair-naturally/

Gilbert, K. (2013). *Natural beauty.* London, UK: CICO Books.

Gladstar, R. (2014). *Herbs for natural beauty.* North Adams, MA: Storey Publishing.

Gladstar, R., & Clare, B. (2010). Herbal Preparations III. Tai Sophia Institute. Laurel, MD.

Hoffmann, D. (2003). *Medical herbalism: The science and practice of herbal medicine.* Rochester, VT: Healing Arts Press.

Hunt, R. (2018). Rough it up hair mud for fine hair and max texture. Retrieved from https://roxiejanehunt.com/2013/11/rough-hair-mud-mustache-wax/

Igler, B. (2016). Making herbal medicines workshop. California College of Ayurveda. Nevada City, CA.

Keville, K., & Khalsa, K.P.S. (2009). Home remedies for psoriasis. Retrieved from https://www.motherearthliving.com/health-and-wellness/ask-the-herbalist-soothe-psoriasis-with-natural-remedies

Kordsmeier, K. (2017). DIY probiotic turmeric honey face mask. Retrieved from https://rootandrevel.com/turmeric-honey-face-mask/

Kshirsager, M. (2015). *Enchanting beauty.* Twin Lakes, WI: Lotus Press.

Lad, V. (1998). *The complete book of ayurvedic home remedies.* New York, NY: Harmony Books.

Lederle, D. (2017). DIY Bergamot and lime deodorant. Retrieved from https://www.thehealthymaven.com/bergamot-and-lime-deodorant/

LisaLise. (2018). How to: DIY deodorant without baking soda. Retrieved from https://www.lisaliseblog.com/2013/05/how-to-diy-deodorant-without-baking-soda.html

Maacaron, F. (2015). *Natural beauty alchemy.* Woodstock, VT: The Countryman Press.

Mama Rosemary. (2014). *Honey bee chamomile lotion bars.* Retrieved from http://mamarosemary.com/blog/2014/12/15/honey-bee-chamomile-lotion-bars

McIntyre, A., & Boudin, M. (2012). *Dispensing with tradition: A practitioner's guide to using Indian and Western herbs the ayurvedic way.* Great Rissington, UK: Artemis House.

Mountain Rose Herbs. (2011). Love-inspired body care. Retrieved from https://blog.mountainroseherbs.com/love-inspired-body-care-recipes

Neumann, N. (2017). *Glow: The nutritional approach to naturally gorgeous skin.* Salem, MA: Page Street Publishing Co.

New, E. (2017). Homemade summertime deodorant recipe. Retrieved from https://www.frugalfarmwife.com/article/homemade-summertime-deodorant-recipe/

Pole, S. (2006). *Ayurvedic medicine: The principles of traditional practice.* Philadelphia, PA: Singing Dragon.

Ress, J. (2014). *100 organic skincare recipes: Make your own fresh and fabulous organic beauty products.* Avon, MA: Adams Media.

Rose, J. (1972). *Herbs and things.* New York, NY: Grosset & Dunlap Workman Publishing Company.

Rose, J. (1990). *Jeanne Rose's kitchen cosmetics.* Berkeley, CA: North Atlantic Books.

Rose, J. (2000). *Herbal body book.* Berkeley, CA: North Atlantic Books.

Sarah, M. (2017). How to make herbal infused marshmallow root flax seed hair gel. Retrieved from https://www.tamthyme.com/blog/diy-herbal-infused-marshmallow-root-flax-seed-hair-gel

Smith, E. (2008). *Therapeutic herb manual.* Williams, OR: Ed Smith.

Stansbury, J. (2018). *Herbal formularies for health professionals: Volume 1: Digestion and elimination.* White River Junction, VT: Chelsea Green Publishing.

Tierra, L. (1992). *The herbs of life: Health & healing using Western & Chinese techniques.* Freedom, CA: The Crossing Press.

Tourles, S. (2007). *Organic body care recipes*. North Adams, MA: Storey Publishing.

Vance, K. (2015). Natural non-greasy hair pomade and texturizer. Retrieved from: https://www.diynatural.com/homemade-pomade-natural/

Wells, K. (2019a). All-natural herbal hair color recipes. Retrieved from https://wellnessmama.com/5112/natural-hair-color-recipes/

Wells, K. (2019b). Homemade bath bomb recipe: Great diy gift! Retrieved from https://wellnessmama.com/8350/bath-bombs/

Wells, K. (2019c). Natural hairspray recipe. Retrieved from https://wellnessmama.com/11624/natural-hairspray-recipe/

Wells, K. (2019d). Natural liquid foundation recipe. Retrieved from https://wellnessmama.com/27328/liquid-foundation-recipe/

Wells, K. (2019e). Natural mascara recipe. Retrieved from https://wellnessmama.com/24899/natural-mascara-recipe/

Wong, J. (2009). *Grow your own drugs*. London, UK: Collins.

*When it comes to what we put into our bodies,*
*we know that our daily diet has a major influence on*
*how we feel, and practicing a balanced, nourished way of*
*eating (at least most of the time!) gives us the stability and*
*resilience to handle a curve ball when it's thrown our way.*
*We might go a little overboard on chocolate cake every once*
*in a while, but if we eat a healthy diet that's full of veggies,*
*fruit, and healthy proteins and fats most of the time,*
*we're more likely to maintain healthy blood sugar levels and*
*digestive capacity that let us stay in balance, even when our*
*diet gets a little funky. Likewise, by giving our skin routine*
*support on a daily basis, we're giving our skin what it needs*
*to thrive: gentle cleansing, targeted herbal TLC,*
*moisture, and protection.*

BOTANICAL SKIN CARE COURSE